BIOMES

OF THE WORLD

VOLUME 1

The Polar Regions

MICHAEL ALLABY

GROLIER
EDUCATIONAL

About This Set

BIOMES OF THE WORLD is a nine-volume set that describes all the major landscapes (biomes) that are found across the Earth. Biomes are large areas of the world where living conditions for plants and animals are broadly similar, so that the vegetation in these locations appears much the same. Each of the books in this set describes one or more of the main biomes: **Volume 1: The Polar Regions** (tundra, ice cap, and permanent ice); Volume 2: Deserts (desert and semidesert); Volume 3: Oceans (oceans and islands); Volume 4: Wetlands (lakes, rivers, marshes, and estuaries); Volume 5: Mountains (mountain and highland); Volume 6: Temperate Forests (boreal coniferous forest or taiga, coastal coniferous forest, broad-leaf and mixed forest, Mediterranean forest and scrub); Volume 7: Tropical Forests (rain forest and monsoon forest); Volume 8: Temperate Grasslands (prairie, steppe, and pampas); Volume 9: Tropical Grasslands (savanna).

The books each have three sections. The first describes the geographical location of the biome, its climate, and other physical features that make it the way it is. The second section describes the plants and animals that inhabit the biome and the ways in which they react to each other. The final section of each book deals with the threats to the biome and what is being done to reduce these. An introduction in Volume 1 includes a map showing all the biomes described in this set, and a map showing all the countries of the world.

Throughout the pages of this set there are diagrams explaining the processes described in the text, artwork depictions of animals and plants, diagrams showing ecosystems, and tables. The many color photographs bring each biome to life. At the end of each book there is a glossary explaining the meaning of technical words used, a list of other sources of reference (books and websites), followed by an index to all the volumes in the set.

Published 1999 by Grolier Educational, Danbury, CT 06816

This edition published exclusively for the school and library market

Planned and produced by Andromeda Oxford Limited, 11–13 The Vineyard, Abingdon, Oxon OX14 3PX, UK

Project Manager: *Graham Bateman*
Editors: *Jo Newson, Penelope Isaac*
Art Editor and Designer: *Steve McCurdy*
Cartography: *Richard Watts, Tim Williams*
Editorial Assistant: *Marian Dreier*
Picture Manager: *Claire Turner*
Production: *Nicolette Colborne*

Origination by Expo Holdings Sdn Bhd, Malaysia
Printed in Hong Kong

Set ISBN 0-7172-9341-6
Volume 1 ISBN 0-7172-9342-4

Biomes of the world.
    p.   cm.
    Includes indexes.
    Contents: v. 1. Polar regions -- v. 2. Deserts -- v. 3. Oceans -- v. 4. Wetlands -- v. 5. Mountains -- v. 6. Temperate forests -- v. 7. Tropical forests -- v. 8. Temperate grassland -- v. 9. Tropical grassland.
    Summary: In nine volumes, explores each of the earth's major ecological regions, defining important features, animals, and environmental issues.
    ISBN 0-7172-9341-6 (hardcover : set : alk. paper). -- ISBN 0-7172-9342-4 (hardcover : vol. 1 : alk. paper)
    1. Biotic communities--juvenile literature. 2. Life zones--Juvenile literature. 3. Ecology--Juvenile literature. [1. Biotic communities.] I. Grolier Educational (Firm)
QH541.14.B57   1999
577--dc21   98-37524
                                              CIP
                                              AC

Contents

What Is a Biome?

A biome is a natural community of living organisms (plants and animals) that occupies a large area. Such communities are dominated by particular plants, and the animals have features and behavior patterns that enable them to live there. The areas involved are vast: much of the center of the United States is covered by the temperate grassland (prairie) biome, where grasses are the main natural plants. A wide band across northern Canada is covered with conifer trees. This is the boreal coniferous (taiga) biome.

Opinions differ about the number of biomes the world holds. It depends on how they are divided. The classification used here lists ten land biomes: tropical rain forest; monsoon and other seasonal tropical forest; savanna and other tropical grassland; desert and semidesert; "Mediterranean" forest and scrub; temperate grassland; temperate broad-leaf and mixed forest; boreal coniferous (taiga) and coastal coniferous forest; tundra; mountain and highland.

In this set we have sometimes included more than one biome in each volume. Temperate broad-leaf forests, boreal coniferous (taiga) forests, and "Mediterranean" forests and scrub, for example, are grouped within a single volume called *Temperate Forests* since they occupy areas next to each other, and both are dominated by trees.

Similarly, tropical rain forest is grouped with monsoon and other tropical seasonal forest in a single volume, *Tropical Forests*.

This set also includes volumes on oceans and wetlands. Wetlands, such as bogs, marshes, and swamps, are often considered separately from rivers and lakes, but it is usual to regard the oceans as making up a single biome. Oceans cover about 70 percent of the Earth's surface, but many of their inhabitants are highly mobile, and there are no barriers to them traveling. In the *Oceans* volume there is also a section on islands, places that are unique because they are small and separated from the mainland by vast expanses of ocean.

As maps of biomes show, the distribution of land-dwelling plants and animals is determined mainly by climate. It follows, therefore, that biomes broadly reflect latitude. Temperature also decreases with height above sea level, however, so mountains often support

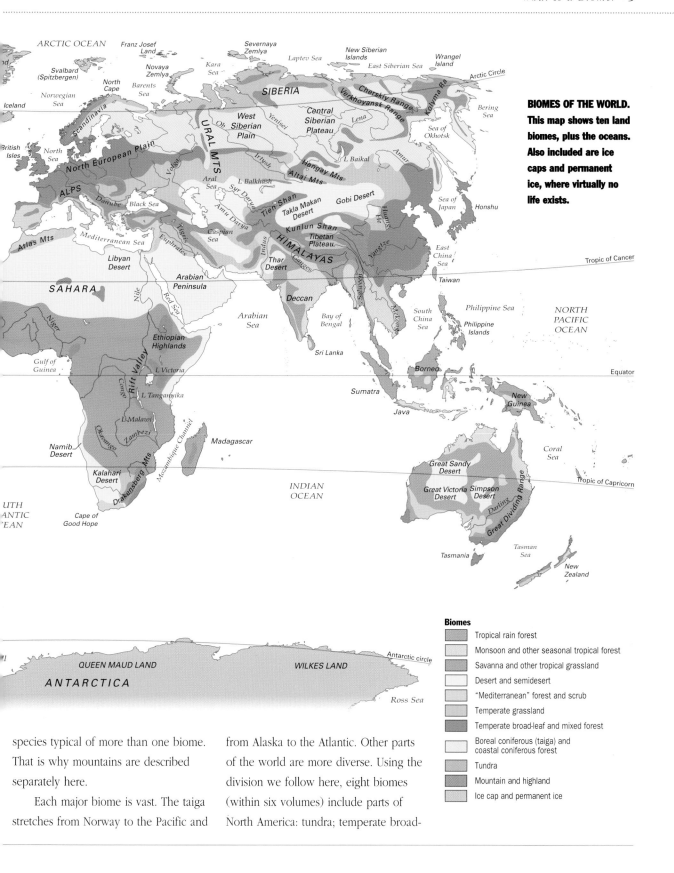

ARCTIC OCEAN

Franz Josef
Land

Severnaya
Zemlya

New Siberian
Islands

Wrangel
Island

Svalbard
(Spitzbergen)

Novaya
Zemlya

Kara
Sea

Laptev Sea

East Siberian Sea

Arctic Circle

North
Cape

Barents
Sea

SIBERIA

Cherskiy Range

Kolyma Ra

Bering
Sea

Iceland

Norwegian
Sea

Scandinavia

West
Siberian
Plain

Central
Siberian
Plateau

Verkhoyansk Range

British
Isles

North
Sea

North European Plain

URAL MTS

Ob

Yenisei

Lena

Sea of
Okhotsk

Amur

Volga

Irtysh

Hangay Mts

L. Baikal

Sea of
Japan

Honshu

ALPS

Danube

Black Sea

Aral
Sea

L. Balkhash

Altai Mts

Syr Darya

Tien Shan

Takla Makan
Desert

Gobi Desert

He

Atlas Mts

Mediterranean Sea

Tigris

Amu Darya

Caspian
Sea

Kunlun Shan

HIMALAYAS

Tibetan
Plateau

Yangtze

Huang

East
China
Sea

Tropic of Cancer

Euphrates

Indus

Thar
Desert

Ganges

Taiwan

Libyan
Desert

Arabian
Peninsula

Deccan

Brahmaputra

SAHARA

Nile

Red Sea

Arabian
Sea

Bay of
Bengal

South
China
Sea

Philippine Sea

NORTH
PACIFIC
OCEAN

Ethiopian
Highlands

Sri Lanka

Mekong

Philippine
Islands

Gulf of
Guinea

Niger

Rift Valley

L. Victoria

Borneo

Equator

Congo

L. Tanganyika

Sumatra

New
Guinea

Java

L. Malawi

Namib
Desert

Okavango

Zambezi

Mozambique Channel

Madagascar

Coral
Sea

Kalahari
Desert

Drakensberg Mts

INDIAN
OCEAN

Great Sandy
Desert

Great Dividing Range

Tropic of Capricorn

SOUTH
ATLANTIC
OCEAN

Cape of
Good Hope

Great Victoria
Desert

Simpson
Desert

Darling

Tasman
Sea

Tasmania

New
Zealand

BIOMES OF THE WORLD.
This map shows ten land
biomes, plus the oceans.
Also included are ice
caps and permanent
ice, where virtually no
life exists.

Antarctic circle

QUEEN MAUD LAND

WILKES LAND

ANTARCTICA

Ross Sea

Biomes

- Tropical rain forest
- Monsoon and other seasonal tropical forest
- Savanna and other tropical grassland
- Desert and semidesert
- "Mediterranean" forest and scrub
- Temperate grassland
- Temperate broad-leaf and mixed forest
- Boreal coniferous (taiga) and coastal coniferous forest
- Tundra
- Mountain and highland
- Ice cap and permanent ice

species typical of more than one biome. That is why mountains are described separately here.

Each major biome is vast. The taiga stretches from Norway to the Pacific and from Alaska to the Atlantic. Other parts of the world are more diverse. Using the division we follow here, eight biomes (within six volumes) include parts of North America: tundra; temperate broad-leaf and mixed forest; boreal coniferous (taiga) and coastal coniferous forest; "Mediterranean" forest and scrub; temperate grassland; desert and semidesert; mountain and highland; and wetlands.

Origins of the Biomes Concept

The word "biome" is just 60 years old. The idea it describes is fairly new, but the history of that idea began with the scientific exploration of the world more than 200 years ago.

The eighteenth century—known as the Age of Enlightenment—was a time of rapid scientific advance. One of the most remarkable of scientific explorers was the German Baron Alexander von Humboldt (1769–1859). In 1799, with his friend Aimé Bonpland—a French surgeon with a keen interest in botany—he went to South America. Over the next five years, wherever they went they made meticulous notes of their observations and collected hundreds of specimens.

Humboldt spent the following 23 years writing and editing the accounts of his travels. Between 1805 and 1834 they were published in 30 volumes as *Voyage de Humboldt et Bonpland*.

Humboldt noticed that plants tend to grow as distinct communities. He observed that the composition of plant communities was related to the climate of the region where they were found. This meant that there was a climatic reason for the way plants are distributed. Humboldt had demonstrated that it is possible to study the geographic distribution of living organisms. This study came to be known as biogeography.

Geographers and Ecologists

Studies of plant distribution could not advance very far until a system had been devised for identifying and classifying plant communities. One of the most influential attempts was made by the German August Heinrich Rudolph Grisebach (1814–79). He described 60 major vegetation types and introduced the idea of "floristic provinces." These are large areas in which the types and communities of plants are fairly similar.

Ecologists then became involved. Theirs was an even newer branch of science. The word "ecology" had been coined in 1866 by the German zoologist Ernst Heinrich Haeckel (1834–1919). It was derived from the Greek *oikos*, meaning "household." Haeckel used it to describe the study of the relationships between living organisms and their chemical and physical surroundings.

One of the most influential ecologists during the early years of this century was the American Frederic Edward Clements (1874–1945). A botanist, he made detailed studies of the plants of the prairies; these led him to propose that plants colonize an area as a series of communities, following one another over time in a succession, until the vegetation attains a final, stable condition, which he called a "climax."

The climax vegetation of, for example, the boreal forest or taiga is dominated by coniferous (cone-bearing) trees such as pines, firs, and spruce. However, these climax plants are not everywhere in the boreal forest. For instance, the aspen, a quite different type of tree, occurs extensively in northern Canada, but not elsewhere in the boreal forest, which extends across Europe as well as North America. Clements had thus devised a system of classification that allowed him to map areas on a large scale, although these dominant characteristic plants were not present everywhere.

So far, almost all the attempts at biogeographical classification had dealt only with vegetation. Scientists knew, of course, that different animal species were found in different parts of the world—notably the French naturalist Georges Leclerc, Comte de Buffon (1707–88), and the English naturalist Charles Darwin (1809–82). These, however, were only observations.

Clements recognized the need for an ecologically based classification system that included both plants and animals, as did his colleague Victor Ernest Shelford (1877–1968)—an ecologist who had trained as a zoologist. The two of them tried to merge their

ideas. The result, which they published in their book *Bioecology* (1939), combined Clements's climax vegetation types with Shelford's animals.

Biomes Defined

Clements and Shelford coined a new word, "biome," that combined the idea of climax vegetation types with the animals that lived there. Thus, a biome is a natural community of living organisms (plants and animals) that occupies a large area. Each biome is dominated by particular plants, and the animals have features and behavior patterns that enable them to live there. Biomes contain characteristic types of

COUNTRIES of the world. When describing parts of a particular biome, we often refer to countries. This map shows all the countries of the world.

plants and animals, but different species occur on each continent. Unrelated species that adapt in the same way to similar conditions often look very alike.

This remains the accepted definition of "biome," and it is still based mainly on the plants that typically are present. Usually, the plants and animals of a biome go together quite naturally. For example, prairie dogs live in temperate grasslands, not in forests; tree squirrels live in forests, not in deserts.

A.	ANDORRA
AL.	ALBANIA
AU.	AUSTRIA
AZ.	AZERBAIJAN
BANG.	BANGLADESH
BEL.	BELGIUM
B.	BOSNIA AND HERZEGOVINA
B.F.	BURKINA FASO
BU.	BURUNDI
CAM.	CAMEROON
C.A.R.	CENTRAL AFRICAN REPUBLIC
CR.	CROATIA
CYP.	CYPRUS
CZ.	CZECH REPUBLIC
DEN.	DENMARK
DOM.	DOMINICAN REPUBLIC
EQ.	EQUATORIAL GUINEA
GAB.	GABON
GE.	GEORGIA
GER.	GERMANY
HA.	HAITI
HU.	HUNGARY
I.C.	IVORY COAST
JAM.	JAMAICA
L.	LEBANON
LUX.	LUXEMBOURG
M.	MACEDONIA
MOZ.	MOZAMBIQUE
NETH.	NETHERLANDS
R.	RUSSIA
RW.	RWANDA
SL.	SLOVAKIA
S.	SLOVENIA
SW.	SWITZERLAND
U.A.E.	UNITED ARAB EMIRATES
ST. VIN.	ST VINCENT AND THE GRENADINES
TURK.	TURKMENISTAN
U.	UGANDA
Y.	YUGOSLAVIA
ZIM.	ZIMBABWE

The Physical World of the Polar Regions

*F*or as far as the eye can see, there is nothing but snow and sky. When the weather is good, the only colors are the clear blue of the sky and the glaring white of the land around you, so bright it hurts your eyes. When the weather is poor, the sky becomes white with whirling snow, and it is impossible to see the horizon.

Pictures show the Arctic and Antarctic—the regions around the North and South Poles—as empty, barren lands where nothing can live. The polar regions are indeed bleak and harsh environments, but they are not uninhabited. Birds, mammals, and fish live in these regions (particularly in the tundra biome, which lies beyond the areas of permanent ice) and have developed remarkable abilities to survive the freezing conditions.

Human populations also survive in the Arctic. Antarctica, which is colder, has no permanent population, but thousands of scientists studying the area live in research stations there. In recent years Antarctica has become a popular tourist destination, although visitors rarely stay long or go far from the coast.

Antarctica is an almost circular continent, except for the projecting Antarctic Peninsula in the west and the deep bays containing the Weddell Sea and, on the opposite coast, the Ross Sea, each of them covered with thick ice. The continent itself is enormous—about 2,800 miles (4,500 km) in diameter—and much larger than

NORTH AND SOUTH. The northern polar region (including the tundra biome)—the Arctic—covers Greenland and parts of North America, northern Europe, and Asia. The southern polar region, the Antarctic, includes the continent of Antarctica. Mountains are included in this map, since at their peaks polar conditions occur.

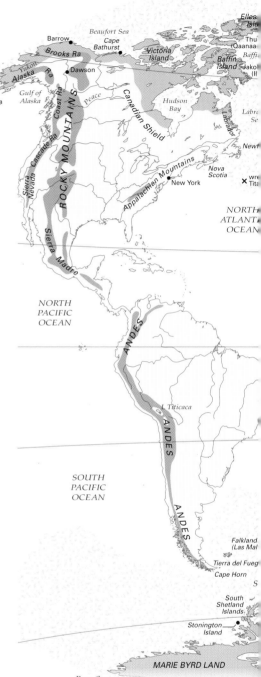

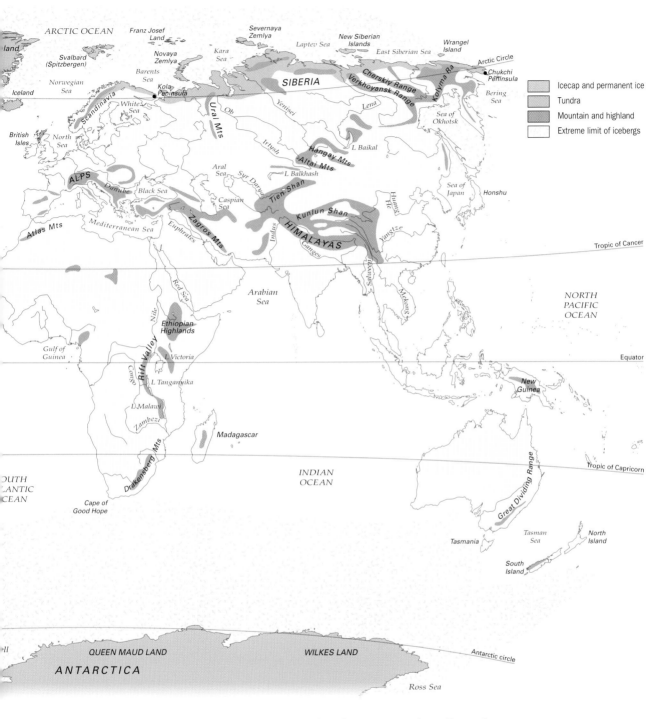

Icecap and permanent ice
Tundra
Mountain and highland
Extreme limit of icebergs

Europe. It is also remote. The distance from Tierra del Fuego, on the southernmost tip of South America, across Drake Passage to the northernmost tip of the Antarctic Peninsula, is about 600 miles (965 km).

Fossil evidence suggests that millions of years ago Antarctica lay near the equator and enjoyed a tropical climate. Coal, made from the remains of plants that grew in the warm swamps, has been found deep beneath the ice.

The Arctic includes most of Greenland, the islands of northern Canada, northern Alaska, northern Siberia, and the north of Norway, Sweden, and Finland. The North Pole is almost at the center of the Arctic Ocean. Most of the year the Arctic Ocean is covered with thick ice, but in summer the sea ice retreats, and a stretch of open sea emerges between the northernmost coasts and the permanent ice.

Approaching the polar regions there are two lines of latitude, 60°30' north and south. These are the Arctic and Antarctic Circles. North and south of them there is at least one day in the year when the sun does not sink below the horizon. For this reason, the lands around the polar regions are sometimes called the "land of the midnight sun," but there is also one day a year when the sun does not rise above the horizon. At the poles there are only two seasons: a winter of near total darkness and a summer of continual daylight, each lasting six months.

LANDS OF ICE

Of all the fresh water in the world, about three-quarters is permanently frozen in the polar regions. The ice takes the form of ice sheets covering the land, snow caps on the mountains, and glaciers—moving masses of ice. Together they occupy an area of more than 5.7 million square miles (nearly 15 million sq. km).

Antarctica contains about 90 percent of the world's ice. The Antarctic ice sheet has an average thickness of 6,900 feet (2,100 m), consisting of about 7.2 million cubic miles (30 million cu. km) of ice.

Greenland, the largest island in the world, has an area of 840,000 square miles (2,175,000 sq. km), of which about 708,000 square miles (1,834 sq. km)—84 percent—are covered by ice. The average thickness of the Greenland ice sheet is 5,000 feet (1,525 m); in places it is much thicker. Around the coast of Greenland a range of mountains projects above the ice. The coast is deeply indented with fjords—long, narrow, deep valleys open to the sea and extending far inland.

ICE SHEETS AND GLACIERS

The table shows the total area of ice and its location. Three-quarters of all the fresh water in the world exists as permanent ice—ice that does not melt in summer. Almost all this ice is in the polar regions, but there is also permanent ice on high mountains, such as the Himalayas, the Alps, and the Andes.

Continent	Area	square miles	sq. km
Antarctica		4,860,250	12,588,000
North America		784,810	2,032,649
(including Greenland, Canadian islands, and Alaska)			
South America		10,232	26,500
Europe		30,682	79,465
(including Arctic islands, Iceland, and mountains)			
Asia		65,899	170,679
(including Arctic islands and mountains)			
Africa		5	12
Oceania		392	1,015
(including New Zealand)			
World total		**5,752,270**	**14,898,320**

A LAND OF ICE.
Antarctica is covered in ice. However, the interior of the continent receives very little snow, and there are extensive ice-free areas.

Even in Antarctica large areas are free from ice. Visit the area and you will see dry, bare rocks. They are called oases or dry valleys, and altogether they occupy an area of about 2,200 square miles (5,700 sq. km).

Both polar regions have arid climates; they are cold deserts, with a similar yearly precipitation to hot deserts. Antarctica is one of the driest deserts in the world. It is covered with ice only because the small amounts of snow it receives never melt, as temperatures do not rise above freezing point. Months of continual sunlight have little warming effect, as the sun is low, spread over a large area, and the snow reflects the radiation.

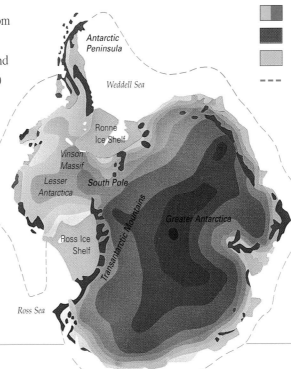

Ice thickness: intervals of 1,640 feet/500 m

Land not covered by ice

Ice shelf

- - - Maximum extent of sea ice

Antarctic Peninsula

Weddell Sea

Ronne Ice Shelf

Vinson Massif

Lesser Antarctica

South Pole

Transantarctic Mountains

Greater Antarctica

Ross Ice Shelf

Ross Sea

THE HIGHEST CONTINENT. Antarctica is divided in two unequal parts by the Transantarctic Mountains. The map shows the dry valleys where there is no ice. Its land surface is an average of about 8,500 feet (2,600 m) above sea level; it is the highest continent.

From Snow to Ice

Each year's fall of snow buries the snow of the previous year. Little by little, the layer of snow thickens and grows heavier, compressing the snow near the base. Snow crystals are pressed closer and closer together until the snow is compacted into ice. This is how polar ice forms. And once it has formed, it starts to move.

Very, very slowly the weight of the ice forces the ice sheet to move outward toward the coast or down a slope. A moving mass of ice is called a glacier. We often think of glaciers as frozen rivers, but this image generally refers to glaciers in valleys. Glaciers can also be moving sheets of polar ice.

THE UNSTEADY EARTH

At one time the polar ice sheets extended much farther than they do today. During ice ages—great periods of cooling—they advanced, and during periods of warming they retreated. The question of why they have advanced and retreated at intervals over about the last 2 million years was addressed in the 1920s by a Serbian climatologist, Milutin Milankovich (1879–1958), who spent 30 years studying the puzzle. Eventually, he concluded that the reason is to be found in variations in the way the Earth spins on its axis and orbits the Sun. In other words, ice ages begin and end as a result of various astronomical events.

Imagine that the Earth's orbit of the Sun follows the edge of a huge disk, with the Sun at its center. This disk is called the plane of the ecliptic. As it orbits, the Earth spins on its own axis, taking 24 hours to make one complete revolution. It is day when our part of the Earth faces the Sun, and night when it faces away from the Sun.

If the Earth's axis were at right angles to the plane of the ecliptic, at noon the Sun would always be directly overhead at the equator. The axis is not at right angles to the plane of the ecliptic, however. It is tilted—at present 23.44° from the vertical. This means that for half the year the Northern Hemisphere is tilted toward the Sun, and it is summer in the north, and for the other half the Southern Hemisphere is tilted toward the Sun, and it is summer there. On just two days in the year—the equinoxes—the noonday Sun is directly overhead at the equator.

The angle of tilt varies—over 40,000 years from 21.5° to 24.5.° This alters the amount by which each hemisphere in turn is warmed by the Sun, so it increases the contrast between summer and winter. A greater angle of tilt will result in a warmer summer and a colder winter.

At the same time, the axis itself "wobbles." The Earth is like a gyroscope or spinning top, its axis like a rod passing through its center and projecting above and below it. When a top spins but is not quite upright, the tip of its axis describes a circle, and the top makes a slow turn at the same time as it spins. This property, called precession, alters the days in the year when the Sun is directly overhead at the equator (the equinoxes). This in turn is called the precession of the equinoxes.

The distance between the Earth and Sun also varies, because the orbit is not quite circular. At present the date at which the Earth is closest to the Sun—called perihelion—is on January 2.

MOVEMENTS OF THE EARTH. The Earth spins on its axis and orbits the Sun, but its movement is not constant. Gradually, the angle of tilt changes. This alters the amount of sunlight reaching the polar regions: the more the Earth is tilted, the warmer the polar regions will be. Axis wobble alters the date at which we are closest to the Sun. The orbit around the Sun also changes shape. At its full stretch we move farther away from the Sun.

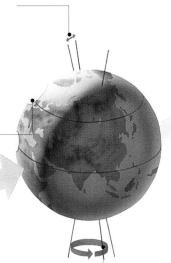

Orbit stretch. The Earth's orbit is slightly elliptical. Over a cycle of 96,000 years, the ellipse varies. This alters the distance between the Earth and the Sun

Axis tilt. The Earth's rotational axis is not precisely at right angles to the path of its orbit (the plane of the ecliptic). At present it makes an angle of 66.56° with the plane of the ecliptic, so it is tilted 23.44° from the vertical. Over a cycle of 40,000 years the angle of tilt increases from 21.5° to 24.5° and back again. This alters the amount of sunlight and heat that places in high latitudes receive in summer and in winter

The Sun's heat is strongest at the equator. Solar radiation is spread over a larger surface area in the northern latitudes than at the equator, and this decreases its warming effect

Axis wobble. The Earth's rotational axis gyrates, like a spinning top, over a cycle of 26,000 years. This alters the time of year when the Earth is closest to the Sun (perihelion). At present perihelion is on January 2, and 13,000 years from now it will be on June 21. Then, Northern Hemisphere summers will be warmer, and winters colder

Thirteen thousand years from now, perihelion will fall on June 21, and 26,000 years from now it will be on January 2 again. If perihelion falls in the middle of summer instead of in the middle of winter (as it does now) summers will be warmer.

Finally, the Earth's orbital path also changes. Sometimes it is almost circular, at other times it is more elliptical. "Stretching" of the orbital ellipse alters the average distance between the Earth and Sun by about 11.4 million miles (18.3 million km) over a cycle of about 96,000 years. We receive more warmth when we are close to the Sun than we do when we are far away; the difference due to orbital stretch amounts to about 30 percent.

The Milankovich Mechanism

No single cycle sufficiently alters the amount of warmth we receive to affect the climate. From time to time, however, the cycles coincide. When all three of them combine to reduce to a minimum the radiation we receive, an ice age begins. When they maximize the radiation we receive, an ice age ends.

Milankovich calculated nine times when the cycles combined to minimize the radiation falling on the Earth and found that that was when ice ages began. Today, most scientists believe that this "Milankovich mechanism" largely explains why ice ages happen but that other factors may also be involved.

ICE SHEETS *(right).* At the height of the most recent ice age, about 18,000 years ago, the North American (or Laurentide) ice sheet covered much of North America, extending south in the United States to what is now Montana. The European (or Fennoscandian) ice sheet covered most of northern Europe. There was less ice in eastern Asia because the climate there was so arid, not because it was warmer.

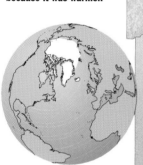

ICECAPS. Today, the north polar icecap covers a fairly small area *(top).* During an ice age, however *(bottom),* it is much bigger.

One of these factors is the Sun itself. (It is important to remember that one should never look directly at the Sun.) Its output of energy varies. This shows as a variation in the number of small, dark patches, called sunspots, on the Sun. They come and go over a cycle of 11 years, but occasionally there is a period of several years when there are many more sunspots than usual, or many fewer.

In 1893 the British astronomer Edward Walter Maunder (1851–1928) discovered there had been very few sunspots between 1645 and 1715, and for a period of 32 years within that timeframe there had been none at all. This "sunspot minimum" coincided with the coldest part of what is called the Little Ice Age.

ICE AGES

The most recent full ice age was at its maximum about 18,000 years ago and ended about 10,000 years ago when the glaciers started to retreat. It was the last of a series of ice ages that began about 2 million years ago. In the United States it is known as Wisconsinian Glaciation and in Britain as Devensian Glaciation.

It began, as all ice ages begin, when summer temperatures in the north were too low to melt the snow from the previous winter. More snow fell the following winter, and it, too, failed to melt when summer returned. As the layer thickened, its weight compressed the snow at the base, packing the crystals together so that the snow turned to ice. The pressure then started squeezing the ice out at the sides so that it flowed away from the center like a very thick liquid. The map (*left*) shows the direction in which the ice spread, until eventually it covered much of North America and Europe.

Because it is white, snow reflects solar energy, so the air above the snow remains cold. Despite the cold, however, some snow is lost from the surface of an ice sheet. If the air is very dry, ice crystals can evaporate directly, without melting first. This is called sublimation. In summer some of the surface snow may melt and then evaporate. Together, these losses are known as ablation. If the rate of ablation is greater than the rate at which fresh snow falls, the ice sheet will grow smaller. It shrinks from the edges, where ablation thins the ice, until it disappears.

Land and Sea Levels

Ice is heavy, and thick ice sheets are extremely heavy. They are so heavy that beneath them the rocks of the Earth's crust are pressed down into the underlying layer, the mantle, and the ground sinks. Then, when the ice disappears, the depressed land begins to rise again, returning to its previous level. It is a very slow process.

Today, some 10,000 years since their ice sheets vanished, Scandinavia is still rising. It was depressed about 3,300 feet (1,000 m), and has now rebounded by about half that distance.

Ice ages also affect sea levels. As water evaporates from the sea and falls as snow over the ice sheets, where it remains, sea levels fall. At the end of an ice age the melting of the ice sheets returns that water to the sea, and the sea level rises.

FREEZING TEMPERATURES

As the Earth orbits the Sun, the equatorial regions face the Sun directly. Its radiation strikes the surface almost vertically. In the polar regions, however, the Sun is low on the horizon. Its rays strike the ground at an angle, so their warmth is spread more thinly.

The tilt of the Earth's axis means that first one hemisphere is turned toward the Sun and then the other, producing our seasons, which become more extreme depending on the distance from the equator. At the poles there is a winter period during which the Sun never rises above the horizon, and a summer period when it never sets. One consequence of this is that in the polar regions the Sun appears to travel parallel to the horizon, remaining low in the sky even in summer.

Winter temperatures are very low. At Thule, Greenland (latitude 76.5°N), the average temperature in January is about –7.5°F (–22°C). Stonington Island, just inside the Antarctic Circle, has an average August temperature of 7°F

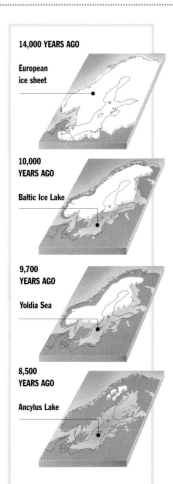

14,000 YEARS AGO

European ice sheet

10,000 YEARS AGO

Baltic Ice Lake

9,700 YEARS AGO

Yoldia Sea

8,500 YEARS AGO

Ancylus Lake

RETREATING ICE. About 14,000 years ago, Norway, Sweden, and Finland lay beneath the European (or Fennoscandian) ice sheet. By 10,000 years ago the ice was retreating. A lake had appeared in what would become the Baltic Sea. As melting continued, it met the North Sea. By 8,500 years ago, a few patches of the ice sheet remained, but much of what is now Sweden was under water, as the land was still depressed by the weight of ice.

THE FROZEN LANDSCAPE
of Vatnajökull in Iceland
covers a fiery, volcanic,
subterranean world
(opposite).

(14°C). Summers are not warm. On Stonington Island January is the warmest month, with an average temperature of about 32°F (0°C), and Thule in July enjoys about 41°F (5°C).

Both Thule and Stonington Island are on the coast, however, where the sea provides some warmth. Inland it is much colder, both in summer and in winter. It is also dry. Thule receives an average 2.5 inches (63.5 mm) of rain and snow a year, giving it a cold desert climate despite being on the coast. Stonington Island is wetter, with an average of 12.5 inches (317.5 mm) a year. (New York City has an average 42.8 inches (1,087 mm) a year.)

THE EARTH'S TILT. The Earth's axis is tilted at 23.5° from the vertical, but it is always tilted in the same direction *(below right)*. As the Earth orbits the Sun, first the Northern Hemisphere, then the Southern, is tilted toward the Sun, and enjoys summer. The effect is greatest at the summer solstice, when the number of hours of daylight reaches a maximum. At the winter solstice the hours of daylight reach a minimum. At the midway points day and night are of equal length (12 hours). These are called the vernal (spring) equinox and the autumnal (fall) equinox. One effect of the tilt *(bottom)* is that the path of the Sun across the sky appears differently to people in different places. At the equator, where the Sun is almost directly overhead at midday, it rises and descends vertically. In the polar regions it travels parallel to the horizon, in summer remaining above the horizon all the time, but in winter never rising above it. In middle latitudes the Sun seems to follow a curved path.

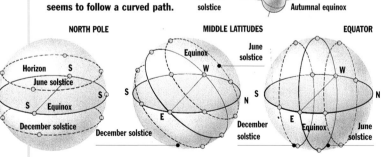

Sea Ice

In many places ice extends to cover the sea surface, making it impossible to see where land ends and the sea begins. This ice forms in two ways. Most obviously, the sea freezes. Sea water freezes at about 28.4°F (−2°C), so the Arctic and Antarctic winters are quite cold enough for sea ice to cover a wide area. In summer the edge of the sea ice recedes, but it does not disappear.

This is the only source of Arctic sea ice (other than icebergs—see page 24), but in Antarctica there are also ice shelves, covering vast areas. These are not made from frozen sea water, but are continuations of glaciers. Antarctic ice shelves are huge. The Ross Ice Shelf in the Ross Sea, for example, is roughly the same size as France.

When the edge of a moving ice sheet (glacier) flows to the coast, it does not stop—it continues down the beach and into the sea. Where the water is shallow, the ice scrapes along the sea bed, its surface above the surface of the water. When it reaches deeper water, it begins to float. Now with water beneath it, the advance of the ice sheet continues, ending when the sea is rough enough to break pieces from its edge or warm enough to melt it.

GLOBAL WINDS AND THE CLIMATES THEY BRING

Cold air is denser than warm air. This is because the temperature of air is a measure of the amount of energy its molecules possess. The more energy they have, the faster they move, the more space there is between them, and so the more room a given amount of air occupies.

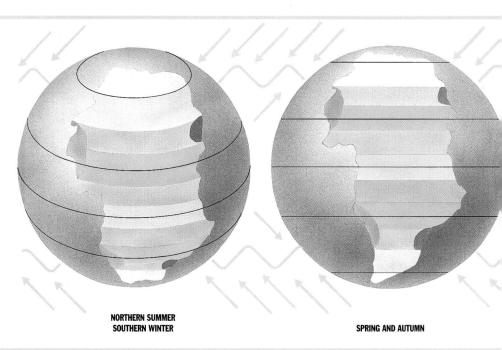

GLOBAL WIND SYSTEMS. The sun shines most strongly in the tropics. Convection currents carry warm air from low to higher latitudes. At lower latitudes cold air flows back to the tropics. This air movement produces the wind systems of the world. Winds at all times of year blow mainly from the east in the polar regions and the tropics, and from the west in middle latitudes.

**NORTHERN SUMMER
SOUTHERN WINTER**

SPRING AND AUTUMN

Cooling the air reduces the energy of the molecules. They move more slowly and pack themselves closer together. The air then occupies less room.

Imagine an area of ground and a column of air above it, reaching all the way to the top of the atmosphere. The denser the air in that column, the more air molecules it will contain, because the molecules are packed tightly together. Because it contains more molecules, the weight of the air column will be greater than that of a column of air that is less dense (that is, one that contains fewer molecules).

Highs and Lows

A barometer measures the weight of air as the pressure it exerts, pushing mercury up a tube or compressing a small metal box. The denser the air, the greater its weight, and so the more pressure it will exert. Cold air is dense, dense air is heavy, and heavy air produces high air pressure. In the polar regions, where the air is always very cold, the atmospheric pressure is high most of the time.

At the equator, where air is warmed intensely, atmospheric pressure is usually low. The warmed air rises and moves away from the equator. Because rising air cools, it becomes very cold. This makes it dense, so it sinks, warming again as it does so, but producing high pressure in the subtropics.

Air flows outward from areas of high pressure and into areas of low pressure. This movement produces winds.

Most of the air flows back toward the equator. When air flows the rotation of the Earth causes it to turn, so it begins to rotate about a vertical axis. At the same time, its movement in relation to the Earth's surface also makes it turn. This tendency of moving air (or water) to

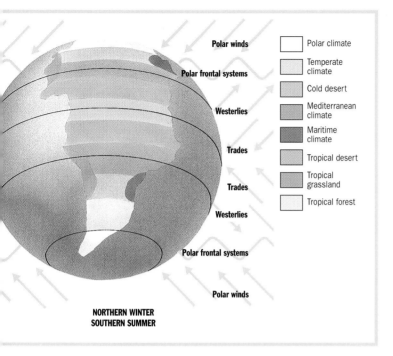

Polar winds
Polar frontal systems
Westerlies
Trades
Trades
Westerlies
Polar frontal systems
Polar winds

☐ Polar climate
☐ Temperate climate
☐ Cold desert
☐ Mediterranean climate
☐ Maritime climate
☐ Tropical desert
☐ Tropical grassland
☐ Tropical forest

**NORTHERN WINTER
SOUTHERN SUMMER**

rotate—like water flowing from a bathtub—produces the trade winds.

Meanwhile, dense polar air spills outward, as easterly winds, carrying cold air into lower latitudes. When it reaches the middle latitudes, it encounters some of the low-latitude air flowing in the opposite direction. Where the two air flows meet, the air rises, producing low surface pressure and westerly winds. At height the air divides again, some flowing toward the pole, some toward the equator.

The Polar Front

The meeting between warm air from the tropics and cold air from the poles produces what is known as the polar front. Low-pressure systems called depressions form beneath this front and bring changeable weather to the middle latitudes. This circulation produces the world's wind systems and the world's climate belts.

THE BEAUFORT SCALE OF WIND STRENGTH

In 1806 Sir Francis Beaufort compiled a scale of wind force to help sailors decide how much sail to use. This scale was soon adopted for use on land.

In the polar regions winds of Force 10 or more blow loose snow and ice around, causing blizzards.

Force 0 — **1 mph or less (1 km/h)**
Calm. The air feels still and smoke rises vertically.
Force 1 — **1–3 mph (1–5 km/h)**
Light air. Wind vanes and flags do not move, but rising smoke drifts.
Force 2 — **4–7 mph (6–11 km/h)**
Light breeze. Drifting smoke indicates the wind direction.
Force 3 — **8–12 mph (12–19 km/h)**
Gentle breeze. Leaves rustle, small twigs move, and flags made from lightweight material stir gently.
Force 4 — **13–18 mph (20–29 km/h)**
Moderate breeze. Loose leaves and pieces of paper blow about.
Force 5 — **19–24 mph (30–39 km/h)**
Fresh breeze. Small trees that are in full leaf wave in the wind.
Force 6 — **25–31 mph (40–50 km/h)**
Strong breeze. It is difficult to open an umbrella.
Force 7 — **32–38 mph (51–61 km/h)**
Moderate gale. The wind exerts strong pressure on people walking into it.
Force 8 — **39–46 mph (62–74 km/h)**
Fresh gale. Small twigs are torn from trees.
Force 9 — **47–54 mph (75–87 km/h)**
Strong gale. Chimneys are blown down, slates and tiles are torn from roofs.
Force 10 — **55–63 mph (88–102 km/h)**
Whole gale. Trees are broken or uprooted.
Force 11 — **64–75 mph (103–120 km/h)**
Storm. Trees are uprooted and blown some distance. Automobiles are overturned.
Force 12 — **More than 75 mph (120 km/h)**
Hurricane. Devastation is widespread. Buildings are destroyed.

THE POWER OF ICE

Early in the last century some Swiss scientists were puzzled by certain boulders found here and there on the plains of northern Europe. These boulders were made from rocks quite different from the bedrock beneath them. Clearly, something had transported them to their present positions. The scientists concluded the boulders must have been pushed by glaciers, but there were no glaciers anywhere near them. Although Swiss glaciers—which the scientists knew very well—often made strange creaking noises, no one had ever seen a glacier move. The boulders seemed to suggest that glaciers move, and that once they extended much farther across Europe than they do now.

One of the scientists was Jean Louis Rodolphe Agassiz (1807–1873). He was a zoologist specializing in fossil fish, but he and some friends took to spending their vacations exploring glaciers. In 1839 they found a hut that had been built on a glacier in 1827 and in 12 years had moved about a mile. They drove a straight line of stakes firmly into the ice across the glacier, from one side to the other. Two years later, the line was no longer straight. The stakes had moved, and those in the center of the glacier had moved farthest. Agassiz and his friends had proved that glaciers move, and he calculated that they had extended much farther some thousands of years ago.

Ice That Flows

Although it flows, a glacier is not a river that has frozen solid. It begins as an ice sheet made from compacted snow called firn. When the firn sheet has grown thick enough for its upper layers to stand higher than the surrounding land, the ice is ready to flow. Squeezed outward by the immense weight of overlying ice, the edges of the sheet start to move, and the ice seeks the easiest route downhill.

Driven by the weight behind and above it, the glacier tears away plants, soil, and loose, projecting rocks. Some of this debris is pushed to the sides, some forced ahead of the advancing ice. Rocks heaped up by a glacier form a "moraine." Those to the sides of the glacier are lateral moraines, those at the foot terminal moraines. Where two glaciers flow into each other, there is usually a line of medial moraine.

There is no shortage of loose rocks. They are dislodged by the action of water seeping into cracks in summer, freezing in winter (expanding and widening the cracks), then melting during

A LANDSCAPE DURING GLACIATION *(right)*. The valleys are occupied by wide glaciers. Rocks and soil embedded in the glaciers erode the valley floor and sides much more powerfully than the rivers did, cutting deeper as they are swelled by ice from tributary glaciers. Frost shatters the mountain tops, and the heads of the glaciers cut back into the mountain slopes. The melting lower end, or "snout" of the glacier sheds rock, sand, and gravel.

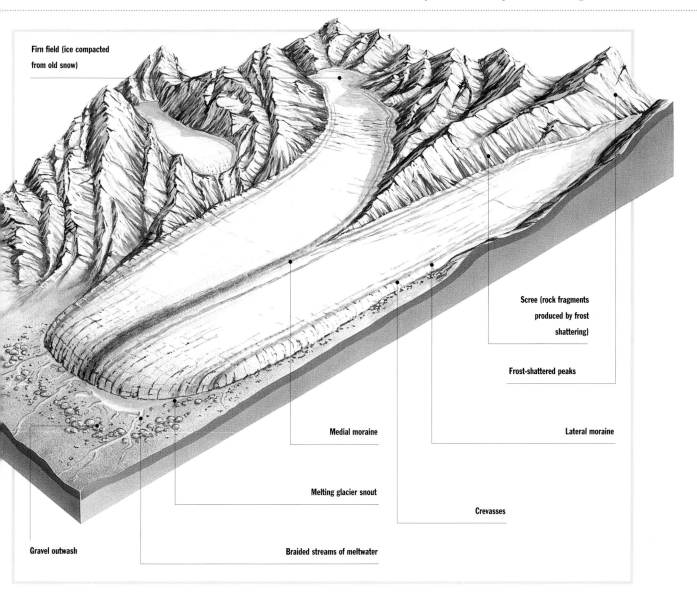

Firn field (ice compacted
from old snow)

Scree (rock fragments
produced by frost
shattering)

Frost-shattered peaks

Medial moraine

Lateral moraine

Melting glacier snout

Crevasses

Gravel outwash

Braided streams of meltwater

STAUNING'S ALPS in eastern Greenland *(left)*. A tongue of ice projects from the edge of the ice sheet, forming a short valley glacier. Rising temperatures since the end of the last ice age caused its lower end to melt faster than pressure from the ice sheet could push it forward, so the glacier retreated.

the following spring. The mechanism is called frost shattering. Over the course of many years small rock fragments produced in this way can accumulate as scree down the side and at the base of a slope.

Glacial Valleys

Where it finds softer rocks bordered by hard rocks the glacier carves a valley, becoming a "valley glacier." The rocks beneath and to the sides are scoured smooth, often with grooves—

called striations—that are made by the sharp corner of a harder rock being dragged along by the ice. Glacial valleys are wide and U-shaped, unlike the narrow, V-shaped valleys that are formed by rivers.

Glaciers can merge, as rivers do, but again there is a difference. Where two rivers join, the beds of both are at the same height. Where glaciers join, it is their surfaces that are at the same height. Their beds are usually at quite different heights. When the glaciers disappear,

A PINGO *(opposite).* **Pingos form in frozen, swampy ground when the surface of a permafrost layer thaws and accumulated water freezes, pushing upward as it does so. Over many years a pingo can reach a height of up to 200 feet (60 m).**

GROUND LOSS. The permafrost layer contains earth that is permanently frozen. In this layer, water held between particles of soil freezes, more water is drawn up from below, and the ground becomes saturated. The overlying active layer of soil acts as an insulating layer. If this is removed, part of the permafrost layer melts. The water runs away, decreasing the volume of the soil, and the land subsides.

the two valleys they leave are at different heights. The upper one is called a hanging valley. If a river flows along it, there will be a waterfall down the side of the other, main valley.

Where a Glacier Ends

The lower end of a glacier is called the snout, because quite often it curves upward where it has flowed against very hard rock and started to climb over it. Glaciers lose ice all the time. Some evaporates (sublimes), and some melts in summer and then evaporates. The warmer the climate, the more ice the glacier loses. At the snout ice is melting, making the edge of the glacier retreat. It does this at the same rate as pressure from behind is pushing it forward.

The snout cannot move forward, because it is losing ice too fast, but neither can it retreat. It remains in the same position. Should the climate become warmer, the rate of melting might exceed the rate of advance, so the glacier would retreat. Should the climate become colder, the rate of advance might exceed the rate of

melting, so the glacier would move farther down the valley.

PERMAFROST AND PINGOS

Beyond the permanent ice the ground may also be frozen. This frozen earth is called permafrost. Although the surface soil thaws in summer, the water in the lower layer remains as ice. Carcasses of Ice Age animals have been preserved for thousands of years in the permafrost layer.

Active layer

Removal (initial ground loss)

Total ground loss

Water loss

Permafrost

Near the edge of an ice sheet there are dome-shaped hills called pingos. They form when, year after year, water is trapped between the permafrost and new ice. In winter the water freezes, expanding and pushing the ground upward as it does so. Where a pingo melts, it can leave a hollow that fills with water and that may be the size of a lake.

Other smaller pools, many of them circular, may form in hollows made by glaciers that have disappeared or in depressions where moraines have blocked the drainage.

PATTERNED GROUND AND PINGO

PATTERNED GROUND. When the surface of frozen ground thaws, rocks may slide downhill on the mud. Repeated freezing and thawing produces patterns of polygons and stripes

PINGO. A hill with a core of ice that grows a little each year. If the ice melts, the pingo collapses; a large pingo can leave a hollow the size and shape of a volcanic crater

ICEBERGS

As the temperature falls and winter begins, the surface of the sea acquires an oily look. Too small to see, ice crystals are forming, then joining together in patches. This is called frazil ice.

After a time areas of the sea surface will become slushy as the frazil ice grows thicker. Patches of frazil ice bump against one another until they form distinct pieces of wet ice. It is now "pancake ice," and as patches of it join and freeze together, most of the surface becomes covered. Once the ice is more than 2 inches (5 cm) thick, it is known as young ice; it is called winter ice when it is more than 8 inches (20 cm) thick. The ice may then have built up over years. Ice more than a year old is called polar ice. Winds and currents carry this ice across the sea and pile it into shapes, such as hummocks, mounds, and flat sheets called floes.

Eventually, these sheets and hummocks pack together and the sea is completely covered. It is then called pack ice, and ships can be gripped by it, unable to move. The constant movement of the ice can crush all but the strongest ships. Icebreakers, ships made especially strong and with powerful engines, are used to keep important channels clear of ice.

In summer the pack ice melts partly, but over the North Pole itself it is permanent. Its winter extent is well known, and the ice presents no danger to ordinary shipping. It is only those vessels needing to land people at research stations in the Antarctic that need to time their journeys carefully so that they leave before the pack ice can trap them. Sailors have ample warning of pack ice. A white gleam of light just above the horizon, called ice blink, caused by reflection from the ice, is a sure sign. So too is a change in the appearance of the sea. It becomes smoother, because the distant ice is damping down the water movement.

Pack ice has not been the cause of major disasters, but icebergs have. On the night of April 14–15, 1912, it was a collision with an iceberg near Newfoundland that sank the luxury passenger liner, *Titanic,* on its maiden voyage. That particular iceberg had drifted south into the western North Atlantic from the Jakobshavn glacier on the west coast of Greenland. Nowadays the oceans are monitored constantly for icebergs, and their exact positions are tracked and reported to ships.

ICEBERGS *(above),* drifting away from the Jakobshavn glacier, on the west coast of Greenland.

GLACIERS AND ICEBERGS *(right).* As glaciers flowing from the Greenland ice sheet reach the sea, their crevasses deepen and widen until pieces of ice —icebergs—break away. Greenland glaciers produce about 10,000 icebergs a year, and they can survive at sea for two years or more.

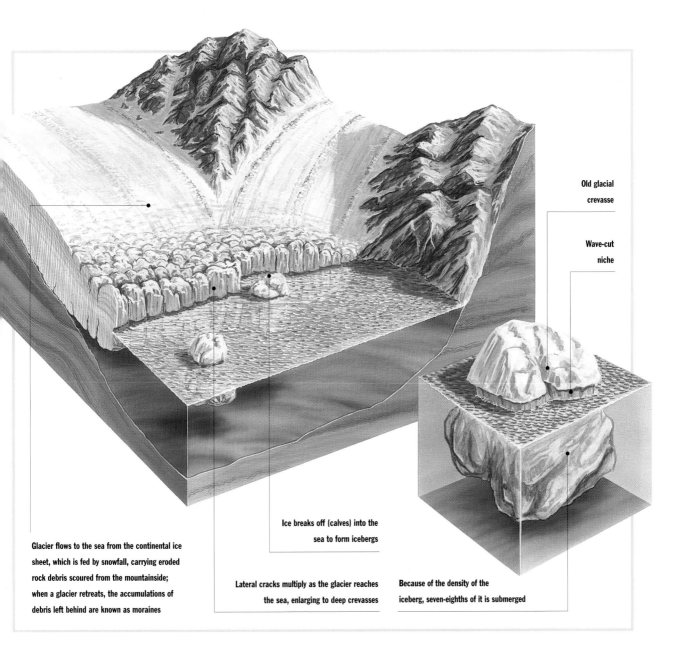

Old glacial crevasse

Wave-cut niche

Glacier flows to the sea from the continental ice sheet, which is fed by snowfall, carrying eroded rock debris scoured from the mountainside; when a glacier retreats, the accumulations of debris left behind are known as moraines

Ice breaks off (calves) into the sea to form icebergs

Lateral cracks multiply as the glacier reaches the sea, enlarging to deep crevasses

Because of the density of the iceberg, seven-eighths of it is submerged

Arctic icebergs originate in Greenland, Svalbard (Spitzbergen), Franz Josef Land, and Novaya Zemlya, where the central ice sheets produce valley glaciers that reach and cross the coast. Where these glaciers enter water deeper than their own thickness, they float, but the constant movement of currents and tides gradually weakens them.

During their travels on land glaciers develop deep cracks called crevasses. Once in the water, being repeatedly lifted and dropped by the currents, the crevasses grow wider and deeper until the entire glacier snaps, detaching a huge chunk of ice. The breaking away of an iceberg is called calving.

Arctic icebergs contain soil and rock fragments scoured by the glacier of which they used to be part. Often this makes them a dirty color, and they are quite dense. One cubic foot of Arctic iceberg weighs about 56 pounds (900 kg per cu. m). They vary in size and shape, but many rise more than 200 feet (60 m) above the sea surface, and extend up to 800 feet (245 m) below it, and they can be up to half a mile (0.8 km) long.

Along the northern coasts of Canada and Siberia ice sheets extend over the sea. From time to time big, fairly flat pieces of ice up to 160 feet (49 m) thick break off and become "ice islands" that can drift for years.

In the Antarctic icebergs are different; there they calve from the ice shelves. They carry no debris from having crossed land, so the ice is cleaner and often blue in color. The icebergs themselves have a large surface area, but are fairly flat, and rarely measure more than about 150 feet (45 m) in height.

Breaking Up

Once adrift in the ocean icebergs may survive for many years. Because so much of their enormous bulk lies below the surface, it is ocean currents, rather than the wind, that direct their movement. But as they drift, they gradually start to melt, and wind and waves break large chunks from them. This can destabilize them and sometimes causes them to capsize.

In time they break up into smaller chunks, at first about the size of a house, called bergy bits. These then break up into smaller pieces, "growlers," less than 30 feet (9 m) long, before finally disappearing.

POLAR SOILS

Soil is a mixture of tiny mineral particles—grains of rock—and the decayed remains of organisms. It starts forming when rocks expand and contract as they are alternately heated and chilled by the weather. When water seeps into cracks and crevices between them, it freezes and expands—shattering the rocks—and then melts and flows away. Small pieces of rock are carried by water and wind, colliding with each other so that they break into smaller particles.

At the same time, the rocks are attacked chemically. Rainwater is naturally slightly acid, and some of the chemical ingredients of rocks react with the acid, forming soluble compounds that are washed away. Water drawn upward from deep below the ground carries substances dissolved in it, and these, too, react with rocks. Together these physical and chemical processes are called weathering.

Next, living organisms start to arrive, because rock particles contain substances on which they can feed. Lichens are often the first to appear. They can grow in sheltered places on bare rock, and their remains provide food for mosses. Eventually, small herbs appear, their roots held securely in the crevices between the rocks. Tiny animals arrive to feed on the plants and their remains. Little by little, soil is formed

SOIL TYPES. Soil forms through the physical and chemical weathering of rock and the accumulation of decaying organic material. These processes need water, warmth, and sunlight, for plant growth. In the tropics soils are deep. In polar regions soil development is slowed by the cold climate, and soil is sparse.

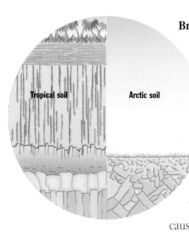

Tropical soil   Arctic soil

from the disintegrated rock particles and partially decomposed organic matter.

The speed at which this happens depends on the climate. In order to grow, plants need sunlight, warmth, and water. If any of these ingredients is missing, the rate of soil development will be very slow.

In the polar regions, where the winter is dark and long and temperatures are so low, even in summer plant growth is restricted, as roots cannot penetrate the permafrost. The topmost layer of soil, which thaws briefly in summer, contains all the decayed plant material, but rock lies not far below.

SPOTTED TUNDRA.
Thousands of years of alternate freezing and thawing of the upper soil layer may have produced this pattern of hummocks and furrows, marked by bands of vegetation.

The Natural World of the Polar Regions

Summers are short, winters long, and most of the year the ground is frozen. Yet the polar regions are not barren. A surprising variety of plants and animals thrives under these harsh conditions.

Beyond the edge of the permanent ice lies the tundra—a land of sedges, mosses, grasses, and lichens growing in patches interspersed by pools and bare rock. The tundra forms a belt across North America, Europe, and Asia, where it extends deep into Siberia. To the south the tundra gradually gives way to the broad belt of coniferous forest often known by its Russian name: the *taiga*. There is much less tundra in Antarctica, because there is much less land beyond the edge of the ice.

Although the area is harsh and inhospitable (tundra means "barren land" in Finnish), it is home to those species that can tolerate its conditions and seize the opportunities it offers.

The warmth does not last long enough for annual plants to complete their life cycles in one year. Consequently, almost all the plants of the tundra are perennials, surviving the winter and growing rapidly during the short summer.

The only woody plants in the tundra are dwarf trees, such as dwarf birch (*Betula nana*)

A TUNDRA ECOSYSTEM.
Slow-growing lichens, mosses, and grasses are primary producers. Herbivores eat grasses and other plants. Carnivores feed on animals. They are all part of the food chain.

Components of the ecosystem

1	Heather family plants	5	Peat
2	Mosses and lichens	6	Permafrost
3	Marsh grass	7	Caribou
4	Cotton grass	8	Arctic hare
		9	Ptarmigan
		10	Arctic lemming
		11	Snowy owl
		12	Wolf
		13	Arctic fox

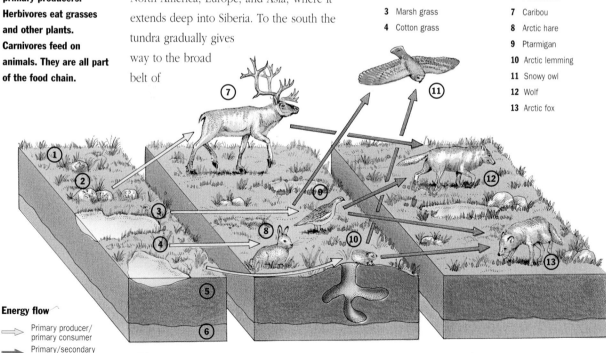

Energy flow
⇨ Primary producer/ primary consumer
➡ Primary/secondary consumer

Primary producers　　**Herbivores**　　**Carnivores**

and several dwarf species of willow (*Salix*), which grow barely more than 3 feet (90 cm) tall.

As soon as the temperature begins to rise, ice patches thaw to become ponds and lakes, hard ground becomes bog (called muskeg). Plants produce leaves and flowers, and insects emerge. If you visit the tundra in summer, you need to wear netting to protect your face from swarms of midges and mosquitoes.

Insects and plants are food for ground-dwelling birds, such as ptarmigans, and for small mammals, such as hares, voles, and lemmings.

These in turn are hunted by wolves, foxes, and snowy owls. The region also supports songbirds and small carnivores, such as weasels, as well as larger ones, such as bears.

Larger mammals include the caribou (*Rangifer tarandus*), which can survive on the sparse vegetation. Like many other animals of the tundra, caribou can be found in both Europe and North America. (In Europe they are known as reindeer.) In winter they feed on lichen, especially a species known as reindeer moss (*Cladonia rangiferina*).

IN THE FALL chlorophyll breaks down in the leaves of the black or alpine bearberry (*Arctostaphylos alpina*), revealing the red of the carotins they contain.

Permanent human populations live in the Arctic. The Inuit, sometimes called Eskimos, are the most numerous and are found in Greenland, northern Canada, and eastern Siberia. There are several distinct groups, speaking different dialects. Traditionally they lived by fishing and hunting, although since the 1950s they have increasingly moved to towns.

In Lapland—a region mainly within the Arctic Circle consisting of the far northern parts of Norway, Sweden, Finland, and Siberia—the nomadic inhabitants, the Lapps, hunt reindeer or rear them. Many Lapps live near the coast and live by fishing.

Farther east, a number of peoples inhabit northern Siberia. The Yakut in northeastern Siberia live by hunting, trapping, and fishing. They were once nomads, and some still are, but most have settled and are engaged in farming.

The Chukchi people of the Chukchi Peninsula herd reindeer for a living, while the Aleuts, who inhabit the Aleutian Islands, between the North Pacific and the Bering Sea, hunt marine mammals, such as whales and seals. The Aleuts are Native Americans, despite living in islands that belong to Russia. Their numbers have fallen drastically in this century; now there are probably no more than 2,000.

PLANTS OF THE TUNDRA

In winter icy winds whip up the fine, loose snow, driving it horizontally with terrible force. Wind force is often measured on a scale (0–12) devised in the 19th century by the British admiral Sir Francis Beaufort (see page 19). In polar regions gales of Force 10, with speeds of 55–63 mph (88–102 km/h), are common. Tall plants would not be able to withstand such fierce "snow-blasting," but the tundra plants are lowgrowing. Lichens cling to the rocks; mosses, algae, and fungi are found in rock crevices.

Grasses grow on drier ground, sedges where it is wetter. Cotton sedge (*Eriophorum vaginatum*) forms tussocks on better-drained land. In late summer its flowers turn into tufts of what looks very much like cotton. It is also called cotton grass.

Here and there, a few woody plants manage to flourish, such as alpine bearberry (*Arctostaphylos alpina*), dwarf willows, and birch, as well as some shrubs that are common in lower latitudes, such as bilberry (*Vaccinium cespitosum*) and crowberry (*Empetrum nigrum*). They are smaller than their southern relatives.

In summer various flowers (including flowering herbs) emerge. All the plants are perennials and start their reproductive cycles as the hours of daylight increase.

SHRUBS OF THE ARCTIC TUNDRA *(below)* **are lowgrowing.**

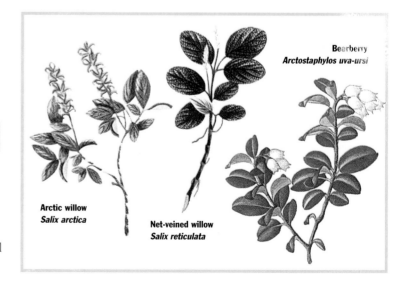

Bearberry
Arctostaphylos uva-ursi

Arctic willow
Salix arctica

Net-veined willow
Salix reticulata

The soil overlying the permafrost is thin, and it contains few plant nutrients. This may be another reason the plants are small. Some have adapted in other ways: attached to the roots of some members of the rose family (Rosaceae) are nodules containing bacteria that can fix atmospheric nitrogen. In this respect (but not others) these plants resemble legumes. One of them is the mountain avens (*Dryas octopetala*).

Pollination

Flowers of the tundra have little time to produce flowers, fertilize them, and release seeds, and there is much competition for the few pollinating insects. Most insects of polar regions feed either on mammals or on rotting wastes; few feed on plants. To attract those that do, most of the herbs have very colorful flowers, and many appear very suddenly. Mountain sorrel (*Oxyria digyna*), for example, forms flower buds at the end of the summer, when the hours of daylight decrease to less than 15. The buds stay tightly shut through winter and open the following spring, as the days begin to grow longer. This way the plant has flowers ready for the first insects to come onto the scene. Once these have been fertilized

THE ARCTIC BELL (*Cassiope tetragona*), a dwarf shrub of the tundra, has tiny leaves pressed close to its stem. It grows very slowly but is capable of photosynthesizing (producing sugars from carbon dioxide and water using light energy) for many seasons; it lives for up to 15 years.

and seeds formed, there is time for the plant to grow new buds.

Even so, insect pollination is unreliable, and some plants reproduce by other means. The spider plant (*Saxifraga flagellans*) is a close relative of *S. stolonifera*, a popular houseplant known as mother-of-thousands because of the reproductive technique the plants use. They produce long stems called runners, red ones in the case of the spider plant, which creep along the ground. Buds develop at intervals along them, and each bud grows into a bulbil—a small bulb that breaks off, puts down roots, and grows into a new plant.

GOOD TIMES AND BAD

It is widely believed that from time to time lemmings commit mass suicide by running into the sea or throwing themselves from cliffs. This is a good story, but unfortunately it is not accurate. What is true is that the lemming population goes through cycles of growth and decline, and sometimes the lemmings migrate in large numbers in search of food. During their migrations it occasionally happens that they meet a cliff and the pressure of those behind pushes the leaders over the edge. Sometimes lemmings drown trying to cross a sea that seems to them no different from the rivers they crossed earlier. The deaths are accidental, not deliberate, and they are rare.

The mainly nocturnal (active at night), somewhat quarrelsome, Norway lemming (*Lemmus lemmus*) undertakes mass migrations. All lemmings experience cycles of "boom" and "bust," and what happens to these small rodents has widespread effects on other species.

Lemmings are rodents belonging to the same subfamily (Microtinae) as voles, and they feed on plants. Like other small animals, lemmings spend the winter in tunnels beneath the snow, where they are sheltered from the biting wind. They produce young throughout the year, except during the freeze at the onset of winter and the spring thaw. No one knows why their numbers increase the way they do, but while food is available, baby lemmings will grow up to eat it.

Every three to six years their numbers increase, although in this harsh environment lemmings are never numerous. In Barrow, Alaska, they have been counted at a maximum density of about 10 per acre (25 per hectare), but the vegetation cannot survive grazing by so many lemmings. After they have fed all summer and then all winter, the ground is left bare. That is when lemming numbers fall in Barrow to about 1 to every 2.5 acres (1 per hectare).

Birds of Prey

Lemmings are an important source of food for all the carnivores of the Arctic. When the lemming population is strong, there is ample food for the wolves, weasels, foxes, and—most of all—the snowy owl (*Nyctea scandiaca*), which hunts by day. When lemming numbers fall, however, the

THE SNOWY OWL *(Nyctea scandiaca)* hunts by day, feeding mainly on lemmings and voles. When these are scarce, they move south.

If you are fortunate enough to see a snowy owl, you will not mistake it for any other bird. It is big—up to 2 feet (60 cm) long—and pure white, with a very round head. Owls hunt in open country, especially around the shores of lakes and over marshes, gliding silently in search of prey, swooping down on animals, and killing them with their talons.

ARCTIC DEER: VEGETARIANS

Voles and lemmings are not the only Arctic vegetarians. There are also Arctic deer, including the caribou (*Rangifer tarandus*) and moose (*Alces alces*).

The caribou are not especially large animals, standing about 40–48 inches (100–120 cm) tall at the shoulder. Those living in Svalbard—a Norwegian archipelago in the Arctic Ocean—are even smaller, often less than 36 inches (90 cm) tall. They are a rather variable gray or brown in color, growing a paler coat in winter than in summer. Those in the far north are almost white.

Both sexes of caribou have antlers. The antlers of the females are smaller and simpler than those of males. In all other deer only the males have antlers.

In summer they eat grass and other plants, and in winter they scrape away the snow to find reindeer moss. Caribou use their feet, not antlers, to scrape for food. Their feet are very broad, which helps spread the weight of the animal and makes it easier for them to move across soft snow and marshy ground.

The moose is the largest of all deer and, despite its size, can run at up to 35 mph

Summer coat

Winter coat

THE RUDDY VOLE (*Clethrionomys rutilus*) changes color in winter. It lives along the southern edge of the tundra, where there are a few trees.

Boxing

Wrestling

LEMMING BEHAVIOR. The Norway lemming (*Lemmus lemmus*) becomes more aggressive as population pressure increases the competition for food.

Threatening

hunters go hungry. Some wander south in search of food; they may even be seen on the outskirts of towns. Their sudden appearance in a region is called an irruption.

Snowy owls can fly much faster and farther than the mammals can walk, and they are sometimes seen as far south as the northern United States.

(56 km/h). A male (bull) stands up to 7 feet (2.1 m) tall at the shoulder and has big, flat antlers with about eight points. Females (cows) are smaller and have no antlers. They have a distinctive long, drooping muzzle.

Unlike caribou, moose are solitary for much of the time, although they often gather in small groups in winter. Their diet consists of grass, herbs, and tree bark.

WOLVERINES: CUNNING SCAVENGERS

Both deer are hunted by wolves, and from time to time they have to defend themselves against one of the fiercest predators, the wolverine (*Gulo gulo*). This is a member of the family (Mustelidae) that includes weasels, ferrets, minks, and polecats. The wolverine is about 3 feet (90 cm) long, not counting its bushy 6-inch (15-cm) tail; it looks rather like a small bear.

The wolverine can produce a foul-smelling liquid from its anal glands like a skunk, and for this reason it is sometimes known as the skunk bear. It is also called the glutton, because centuries ago people believed it would eat until it could eat no more, make itself vomit, and then return to its meal, repeating this behavior until no food was left. This is not true.

Like most carnivores, wolverines will feed on the carcasses of animals killed by other predators; they will not pass up the chance of a meal. What it cannot eat immediately the wolverine often tears into pieces and stores, sometimes for months, before returning to them. They may then provide food for a nursing mother or freshly weaned young (kits).

Wolverines are frightened of nothing and are very cunning. They will steal from traps without being caught in them, break into cabins to scavenge for food, spraying the interior and making it uninhabitable, and fight any animal that threatens them. A wolverine has been known to attack a bear.

Wolverines usually live alone, but occasionally in pairs. They hunt by day and by night, often by waiting to ambush prey. They are agile creatures and can jump high and climb trees.

Spreading the Weight

Like all animals of the Mustelidae family, wolverines walk with the entire soles of their feet touching the ground (this characteristic is known as plantigrade gait). The large size of their feet helps them move over soft ground by distributing their weight over a large surface area. Caribou also have large feet, but they are heavier, and on very soft ground the wolverine has the advantage.

Wolverine fur also has an advantage. Fur provides insulation by trapping air, which is warmed by the body. But when hair or wool mats, the fibers pack tightly together, squeezing out the air. This results in a reduction of insulation. Wolverine fur does not become matted, and this makes it valuable.

Wolverines are still hunted for their fur, although nowadays such hunting is on a small scale. Inuit peoples traditionally use the fur to trim their parkas.

THE MOOSE *(Alces alces)* **is well able to defend itself against a wolf** *(below)***. A bull moose** *(right)* **is the largest of all deer.**

THE WOLVERINE, or skunk bear *(Gulo gulo) (right)***, fears nothing. Both the wolverine and caribou have broad feet** *(inset)***, but on soft ground the caribou's feet sink into the surface and slow it down. Wolverines live in very remote places** *(far right)***. This makes them difficult to study.**

SOFT, THICK UNDERFUR makes up about 70 percent of the coat of the Arctic fox *(Alopex lagopus)*, allowing it to rest without fear of freezing. It does not even shiver until the temperature falls below −58°F (−50°C).

ARCTIC FOXES: SURVIVING THE COLD

Wolverines are not the only Arctic mammals to have coats adapted for survival during the long dark cold winter. Foxes are among the most adaptable of animals. There are several species, and they have found ways to survive even in the centers of our cities. It is hardly surprising, then, that one species thrives in the high Arctic in latitudes higher than 70°N and never leaves for warmer climes.

The Arctic fox (*Alopex lagopus*) is about 20–25 inches (50–64 cm) long, somewhat smaller than the common red fox. Its small ears are well suited to the cold weather. Ears contain many small blood vessels (you can see this yourself, by the way your ears turn red when you rub them), and as the blood flows just below the skin, it is cooled by the air. Consequently, animals that live in hot climates often have large ears, which help them lose body heat, and animals such as the Arctic fox that live in cold climates have small ears that help them conserve heat.

Most mammals have two types of fur. Next to the skin the underfur is fine and traps a layer of air warmed by the body. Above it the outer fur is coarser, waterproof, and forms a covering that protects the underfur and keeps it dry. Soft underfur makes up about 70 percent of the coat of an Arctic fox. It allows the fox to curl up snugly in a sheltered spot and sleep for long periods with no risk of freezing in even the lowest temperatures.

THE ARCTIC FOX *(Alopex lagopus)* **occurs in two color forms—the white and the blue (really a gray-brown color), each with a different winter and summer coloration. The blue fox is a rarer form. A blue fox vixen "helper" in brown summer coat with her younger siblings (1). An adult blue in winter (2). The white form, in winter coat, attacks a ptarmigan, also in its winter plumage (3). The white form in its brown summer coat (4).**

Changing Color

Changes in fur color serve to camouflage some animals. This is especially important in polar regions beyond the northernmost limit for trees. There is very little cover, and in winter the surface is uniformly white; it is relatively easy to see anything that is colored, even if it lies perfectly still.

In summer the coat of the Arctic fox (*Alopex lagopus*) is brown on the head, back, and tail and paler along the underside of the body. In winter its fur turns white, blending in with the snow in the landscape.

There is also a rarer form of Arctic fox called the blue fox. Its fur is grayish-brown rather than blue. Blue foxes make up only about 1 percent of the Arctic fox population on the American and Eurasian mainland, but on some islands most of the foxes are of this type.

Other Arctic species change color in the same way. The blue hare (*Lepus timidus*) is one of the best known, because it also occurs far south of the polar regions. Its summer coat is brown rather than blue, but in winter it turns white, at least in the north of its range. Farther south the transformation is not always complete. The stoat (*Mustela erminea*), too, often turns completely white in winter.

Many birds wear different plumage in summer and winter, and for some white is the appropriate winter color. The willow and rock ptarmigans (*Lagopus lagopus* and *L. mutus* respectively), for example, are brown in summer and white in winter.

MUSK OXEN: YEAR-ROUND RESIDENTS

The musk ox (*Ovibos moschatus*) does not change color according to the season—its coat is dark brown all year round. A musk ox looks like a shaggy bull, with a coat that reaches almost to the ground, and is superbly suited to life in the open tundra. The coat you see is the coarse outer coat, which keeps out the rain and snow. Beneath it is a dense undercoat made of much finer hair, which is shed in summer. Eskimos use this wool to make a cloth similar to cashmere.

Bulls stand about 5 feet (1.5 m) tall at the shoulder; cows are a little smaller. Their hoofs are broader than those of cattle, helping the oxen move over soft snow and summer mud.

Musk oxen feed on grasses, lichens, and the leaves of woody plants, and in winter they will dig through the snow to find food.

Neither Cattle nor Sheep

Despite their name, musk oxen are not cattle, although they belong to the cattle family (Bovidae). They are more closely related to sheep, as their name suggests: *Ovibos* means "sheep–cattle." The "musk" (*moschatus*) of the name refers to the strong smell the bulls emit during the mating season.

During the last ice age musk oxen lived throughout the Arctic, but today they are found only in parts of Canada and Greenland, north of about latitude 64°N. However, they have been reintroduced in Alaska, Svalbard, and Norway and released into the wild. They were also reintroduced in Sweden and Iceland, although they died out again.

Some people think that musk oxen should be domesticated and raised for their excellent milk, wool, and meat in regions where neither cattle nor sheep can survive.

Strength in Numbers

In summer musk oxen live in herds of up to about 30. During the breeding season older bulls drive out their younger rivals and round up as many cows as they can to form "harems." Later in the year much larger herds form, containing bulls, cows, and the young.

THE MUSK OX *(Ovibos moschatus)* has a thick, coarse outercoat and a dense, fine undercoat that keeps it dry and warm in the Arctic winter. Musk oxen live in herds, sometimes huddling together for warmth *(below)*.

WHEN THREATENED, the adults form a circle around the young *(right)*.

Both bulls and cows have flat, broad horns that curve upward at the tips. Musk oxen are not aggressive, but their horns are formidable weapons, and the oxen will use them in self-defense. When threatened, the adults either line up shoulder to shoulder to face the enemy, with the young behind them, or form a tight circle, facing outward, with the young inside. A herd of musk oxen is more than a match for a pack of hungry Arctic wolves.

Standing shoulder to shoulder and refusing to give ground is, however, no defense against human hunters armed with rifles, and hunting has greatly reduced the numbers of musk oxen.

MIGRATING HERDS

While musk oxen stay in the tundra, herds of Arctic deer migrate. The herds are often enormous. Most are made up of females with

some young males, all led by an older female. Males sometimes form smaller herds, especially in winter.

Reindeer, the European variety, spend the summer in the tundra and then in the fall, at the end of the breeding season, travel fairly short distances to their winter feeding grounds farther south. Caribou, the North American variety, migrate over much longer distances.

Woodland caribou inhabit forested areas from Newfoundland and Nova Scotia across most of Canada. Barren ground, or northern, caribou live in the tundra and along the northern edge of the coniferous forests (forests in which the majority of trees are conifers, such as firs, pines, larches, and spruces) from Greenland to Alaska. These are the caribou that undertake long seasonal migrations. Each spring they assemble in large numbers and march north along fairly regular routes, some heading for the coast, where there are fewer mosquitoes. At the start of winter they return south.

One migration route in the Northwest Territories of Canada runs between Cape Bathurst, about 70°N, southeast to the eastern edge of Great Slave Lake, about 63°N. Another route crosses Alaska, running southeast to the east of Dawson City in Canada.

When the 800-mile (1,300-km) trans-Alaska pipeline was built in the 1970s, it was raised on stilts, partly to allow caribou to pass because the pipe crossed a migration route. This was only partly successful; the caribou preferred to walk beside the pipe rather than underneath it.

Native American and Inuit tribes traditionally used the barren ground caribou for their meat, hide, and antlers, which they made into

implements. The migrations were so regular and the routes so well known that the hunters simply waited for the herds to arrive.

WOLVES: PACK HUNTERS

Wolves also depend on the caribou, and like humans their hunting is made easier by the fact that migrating caribou are not hostile—it is easy to get very close to them.

GRAY WOLF BEHAVIOR. The gray wolf *(Canis lupus)* is highly social. Adults usually mate for life, and related breeding pairs and their pups live together as a pack. In this group wolves are behaving in ways you often see among domestic dogs.

They communicate by body language. The illustration shows the following behaviors:

1 A peaceful greeting. One wolf holds its tail low and its ears back. The wolf is adopting a submissive posture to a more dominant wolf.

2 Pups playing. The pup that has been seized holds its ears back and keeps its mouth closed, showing it is not angry.

3 Pups fighting. One pup holds its front legs stiff as it pushes its litter mate: it is asserting its authority.

THE CARIBOU *(Rangifer tarandus)* **is known in Europe as the reindeer. Caribou live in herds and migrate over long distances.**

The gray wolf (*Canis lupus*) is highly social. Most wolves mate for life and live in packs of up to about 20 individuals, consisting of breeding pairs and their young. Each pack hunts within a range, varying in size from 40 to 400 square miles (100 to 1,000 sq. km), and has a small core area where pups are born and raised and where the wolves can relax.

The pack has a leader, and the members all have ranks. Fights sometimes occur when a subordinate individual challenges a more dominant one in the hope of winning "promotion" within the group, and occasionally the leader may be challenged. Individuals may be driven from the pack as a result of fights, and others leave voluntarily to seek a vacant territory and start a pack of their own. The borders of the range are marked by dominant members of the pack, which urinate in particular places as the pack passes.

Wolves sometimes howl together, probably to advertise their location to other packs. The wolves defend their ranges against trespassers from other packs, although incursions often go unnoticed.

Wolves feed on any small animal they can catch and will eat carrion, but they work in small groups to capture larger prey, including caribou. The wolves spread out as they approach the herd, select an individual caribou, and then separate it from its companions, like sheepdogs separating a sheep from the flock.

POLAR BEARS: THE ULTIMATE HUNTERS

Beyond the tundra along the high Arctic coasts and on sea ice and ice floes lives the largest of all land-dwelling carnivores, the polar bear (*Ursus*—formerly *Thalassarctos* or *Thalarctos*—*maritimus*). Polar bears have long legs and

COMING TOGETHER.
Polar bears *(opposite)* spend most of their time alone, but occasionally a group will congregate around food, such as a whale or walrus carcass, or where the melting of the sea ice has reduced the number of floes. Their encounters are generally peaceful.

HUNTING MACHINE.
The biggest of all land-dwelling carnivores, the polar bear *(Ursus maritimus)* has strong legs and paws and sharp teeth and claws, making it an extremely effective hunter.

necks, small ears, and thick, creamy-white fur, which provides camouflage as well as insulation. Males are often more than 9 feet (2.7 m) with a tail of up to 5 inches (13 cm) long. Females are about 8 feet (2.4 m) long. Despite their size and weight—an adult male may weigh 1,400 pounds (635 kg)—the speed of polar bears makes them effective hunters. They can easily outrun a caribou over a short distance. They are also excellent swimmers. They use their powerful front legs to paddle and can swim for several hours between ice floes.

Polar bears will eat berries and leaves and will take eggs from birds' nests in summer, although meat accounts for most of their diet. They hunt all the animals of the Arctic and scavenge carcasses of animals killed by other predators. When they are on land, they feed mainly on hares, caribou, and musk oxen. In the water they hunt fish, ringed and bearded seals, and seabirds. They have even been known to attack walruses and beluga whales.

Polar bears wander widely in search of food and mates. A bear can cover 40 miles (64 km) or more in a day and up to 700 miles (1,125 km) in a year. They usually follow the sea ice northward in summer and southward in winter. But they tend to remain within a particular area: a Greenland bear is unlikely to visit Alaska, for example. Scientists learned this by tagging and tracking individuals. This, combined with differences in the size of bear skulls from one region to another, suggests that there are several distinct populations. With so large an area in which to wander it is hardly surprising that, except at breeding time, polar bears spend most of their time alone.

Mating

Females mate for the first time when they are four or five years old. Mating takes place from April to June. In November and December pregnant females dig themselves dens in deep snow, often near a coast. Between one and three very small cubs are born in the dens between December and January. They stay in the den until March or April, by which time they will have grown from an average 25 ounces (710 g) to 20 pounds (9 kg), being fed a diet of milk that is more than 30 percent fat. The cubs will remain with their mother for more than a year, and females are able to breed only every second year.

ARCTIC LIFE OFFSHORE

Several species of seal live around Arctic shores, and they are hunted by polar bears. The ringed seal (*Phoca*, or *Pusa*, *hispida*) is the one polar bears catch most often, probably because it is one of the most numerous, with a population counted in millions. There are various populations, but ringed seals are found in all Arctic waters and have been known to travel as far south as California and Portugal. Their dark coats are marked with light-colored rings that give them their common name.

All seals leave the water to rest and give birth, but ringed seals rarely venture onto land. They rest and are born on the ice.

Harp seals (*Phoca*, or *Pagophilus*, *groenlandica*) are also numerous, with a world population probably approaching 4 million, but they are not evenly distributed. There are distinct

A HARP SEAL (*Phoca groenlandica*) with pup. The "harp" refers to the marking on the back of the adult.

A RINGED SEAL *(Phoca hispida)* in a typical resting position beside a hole in the ice.

A HOODED SEAL (*Cystophora cristata*) with pup.

populations off eastern Canada, Greenland, and near the Kola Peninsula, for example. They are very active and fast swimmers, often moving in large groups. The "harp" of their name refers to the shape of a dark mark on the back of the adult males. Seals of the genus *Phoca* are generally fairly small, most growing to about 5 feet (1.5 m) long.

Bearded seals (*Erignathus barbatus*), the only species in their genus, are bigger—more

A MALE WALRUS showing its "walrus mustache" and huge tusks, which in fact are its upper canine teeth. Females also have tusks, but they are smaller. The walrus *(Odobenus rosmarus)* is the biggest of all the seals and sea lions. This one is about 11 feet (3.4 m) long.

The male hooded seal has a curious talent. It can force the lining of one nostril down through and out of the other nostril, inflating it like a red balloon. Alternatively, it can blow out and inflate the whole of its nasal cavity, which is black. These red and black "balloons" are the "hoods" that give the species its common name. A male displays them during the mating season to impress rival males and also to amplify the roars with which he drives away competitors that come too close.

Walruses

Several families of seals and sea lions form the suborder Pinnipedia of carnivorous mammals. Their members vary in size, but the biggest of them all is the walrus (*Odobenus rosmarus*), the only species in the family Odobenidae. An adult male is up to about 11 feet (3.4 m) long.

Walrus skin is about 1 inch (2.5 cm) thick and very wrinkled. Its tusks and "mustache" are distinctive. The tusks are, in fact, very large upper canine teeth, used by males to assert their dominance, and by both sexes to haul themselves out of the water and prop up their heads when they are resting.

The walrus is able to bring its hind flippers forward to help it move on land. This does not mean that it is very mobile, however. It drags itself along, rather than flopping along in the manner of some seals.

Walruses occur near all Arctic coasts. They are very social and can be seen resting in huge numbers, lying half on top of one another on ice floes or beaches. They feed on invertebrates—animals without backbones, such as crabs, shrimps, and mollusks.

than 7 feet (2.1 m) long. They are also prey to polar bears. Much larger than ringed seals, they, too, occur throughout Arctic waters and are fairly abundant. They have no beards, but their whiskers are bigger and more prominent than those of most seals.

The hooded seal (*Cystophora cristata*), measuring about 7.5 feet (2.3 m) long, lives off eastern Canada, Greenland, and northern Scandinavia, occasionally straying farther afield.

LIFE AT SEA: THE WHALES

Whales are also social animals. Some species live in all seas, but others spend their whole lives in polar waters.

There are two main groups of whales: those with and those without teeth. The Arctic whales are principally toothed, and in one case in a very peculiar fashion. The narwhal (*Monodon monoceros*) has two teeth. Those of females remain below the surface of the gum and so does the one on the right side of the male's mouth. The left tooth of the male, however, grows forward, through the upper lip, as a long, spiral tusk, like that of the mythical unicorn. The scientific name of its genus, *Monodon*, means "one tooth," and that of its species, *monoceros*, means "one horn."

The tusk can be nearly 10 feet (3 m) long, on an animal with a body about 16 feet (5 m) long. A very few females grow short tusks, and a very few males grow two tusks. No one knows what the tusk is used for. Perhaps males impress females with it or dominate other males. It appears to have nothing to do with obtaining food, because males with tusks eat precisely the same diet as females. Even without the tusk narwhals would be striking. Their skin is marked with blotches of cream, black, and gray-green.

Narwhals move in groups and are fast swimmers. Like all whales, they must surface to breathe. When they do, the tusks of the males project above the water, so there is no mistaking a school of narwhals. They spend much of their time beneath sea ice and need holes at which to breathe. They congregate in large numbers around these holes and keep them open by head-butting them. That is where Inuit people catch them for their meat and fat (blubber). Narwhals themselves feed on fish and invertebrates. Scientists believe that they catch their food by sucking it into their mouths.

Narwhals belong to the family Monodontidae, which has only one other member—*Delphinapterus leucas*, the white whale or beluga, to give it its Russian name (the Russian word *bel* means "white").

White Whales

White whales are born reddish-brown, turning gray. As the common name suggests, adults are pure creamy white. Apart from their color white whales are recognizable by their small beak and the large swelling, or melon, on their forehead. They are much the same size as narwhals, adults growing to about 16 feet (5 m), and the males are bigger than the females. Also like narwhals, the neck is much more mobile than in most whales, so they can, and do, turn their heads. Unlike narwhals, white whales have up to 20 teeth in both upper and lower jaws.

White whales swim fairly slowly in large or small groups. They feed at the bottom of shallow water on a variety of shellfish and also hunt schools of fish. They are able to work in teams to herd fish into shallow water where they are easier to catch, but they also chase and catch individual fish. They can suck and blow jets of water, a technique they use to dislodge and then catch fish hiding in crevices. Young white whales have to learn to do this. They swim beneath sea ice and, like narwhals, will smash through it to make breathing holes. Females of both species

THE WHITE WHALE (*Delphinapterus leucas*) (middle and bottom) is closely related to the narwhal and is also found throughout the Arctic. The young are born reddish-brown and turn gray, but the adults are pure creamy white. After birth the calf remains very close to its mother.

A MALE NARWHAL (Monodon monoceros) (top). The spiral tusk is the tooth on the left side of the upper jaw. Only the males have tusks, although a very few females have smaller ones. No one knows the purpose of the tusks.

give birth to young about every three years. White whales sometimes enter rivers, and their young are often born in estuaries. Both species live up to 40 years.

Both white whales and narwhals are very vocal, but white whales especially so, and their whistles and clicks are clearly audible over some distance. No one knows the purpose of these sounds. The whales might be keeping in touch with one another, announcing their whereabouts. Mothers may use sound to keep their young from wandering too far.

White whales, and probably narwhals, are often attacked by killer whales (*Orcinus orca*). If they become trapped in shallow water, they are easy prey for polar bears.

BIRDS OF THE ARCTIC

As the sunshine of the lengthening days of late spring melts the snow and warms the ground, fresh grass begins to grow. This grass is more nutritious than the later growth, and birds arrive in vast numbers to exploit it, not so much for themselves as for their chicks. The tundra is a breeding ground for birds.

The snow goose (*Anser caerulescens*) is common in the region. Most snow geese are pure white with a dark pink bill and legs and black wing tips, but there is a variety in North America known as the blue goose; it has a blue-gray body.

Arctic geese are smaller than the geese that spend all year in warmer regions. The snow goose is up to about 30 inches (75 cm) long. Its smaller size means it and its chicks need less food to sustain them, and its eggs are small, so they do not take long to incubate.

The breeding colonies are immense. Losses are high from bad weather, starvation, and predators. Those young that survive have only a few weeks in which to grow strong enough for the southward migration, but there is ample time for feeding during the long hours of Arctic summer daylight.

Before starting their northward migration, the geese develop a layer of body fat. This is a food reserve to see them through the journey and for up to three weeks or so after they arrive, in case spring comes late. Females also need the fat reserves for egg production. Some birds make the flight in one go, but most do it in stages.

The snow goose winters primarily in North America. Its European equivalent, the barnacle goose (*Branta leucopsis*), is about the same size. It breeds on the open tundra or on Arctic cliffs and spends the winter on coasts and estuaries farther south, seldom moving far inland. The brent goose (*Branta bernicla*), or brant, is one of the smallest geese, measuring about 24 inches (60 cm) long. It breeds in the high Arctic but in summer can be found as far south as western France and even Portugal.

The wheatear (*Oenanthe oenanthe*) is barely 6 inches (15 cm) from the tip of its bill to the tip of its tail. However, some move between breeding grounds in eastern Siberia and winter feeding grounds in Saudi Arabia, and between Greenland and West Africa.

THE IVORY GULL (*Pagophila eburnea*) is the only gull with pure white plumage.

ROSS'S GULL (*Rhodostethia rosea*) is distinctively marked with a rose-colored body and a thin black "collar."

McKAY'S BUNTING (*Plectrophenax hyperboreus*) (*right*) lives on land bordering the Bering Strait, connecting the Bering Sea and the Arctic Ocean.

THE SNOW GOOSE (*Anser caerulescens*) (*left and below*) breeds in the tundra and spends the winter farther south.

THE SNOW PETREL *(Pagodroma nivea) (above)* feeds at sea. It breeds on Antarctic shores.

THE SNOWY SHEATHBILL *(Chionis alba) (left)* lives on the coast and islands of Antarctica.

Gulls of the Arctic

Most gulls are light in color, but only the ivory gull (*Pagophila eburnea*) has pure white plumage. It lives in the high Arctic, spending much of its time near the edge of the pack ice, and it seldom lands on water. Its eggs are laid on cliffs and rocky ground, often on the ice.

Ross's gull (*Rhodostethia rosea*) breeds in the swampy tundra of eastern Siberia and lives among ice floes. It is a striking bird with a pale gray back and wings, a white body tinged with pale pink, and a narrow, black collar.

The Arctic tern (*Sterna paradisea*) makes the longest of all bird migrations. It spends the northern summer in the Arctic and the southern summer in the Antarctic, flying about 9,500 miles (15,300 km) between the two.

BIRDS AND SEALS OF THE ANTARCTIC

The snow petrel (*Pagodroma nivea*) and the Antarctic petrel (*Thalassoica antarctica*) are rare outside Antarctic waters. The snow petrel is the only member of its family (Procellariidae) to seek shelter for its nest.

The snowy, or yellow-billed, sheathbill (*Chionis alba*) is also found in Antarctica. It lives in noisy flocks, spending much of its time scavenging whatever it can find along the seashore.

The most famous birds of Antarctica are the penguins. They form the order Sphenisciformes, containing just one family, Spheniscidae, with 16 or 18 species. All are flightless birds with an upright posture and waddling gait. Ungainly on land, they dive and

MIGRATION ROUTES

The wheatear *(Oenanthe oenanthe)* migrates to Greenland, Eurasia, and eastern North America.

Brent geese *(Branta bernicla)* occur throughout the Northern Hemisphere; many winter in northwestern Europe.

The American golden plover *(Pluvialis dominica)* migrates to South America.

swim well, however, with their streamlined body and wings reduced to flippers. They breed in large colonies on the ground, some building simple nests from pebbles.

Penguins are not found in the Northern Hemisphere, but do occur outside the Antarctic. They are also found in New Zealand, South Australia, South Africa, and South America in regions where there are cold ocean currents.

Antarctic Seals

Penguins feed on fish and crustaceans, but once they enter the sea, they must contend with their principal enemy, the leopard seal (*Hydrurga leptonyx*). It is a long, slender animal, about 11 feet (3.4 m) long, with a large mouth. It is a fast swimmer and feeds mainly on penguins, which it catches in the water. The seals of the Southern Hemisphere are very similar to those in the north, although the two groups have evolved independently of one another for millions of years. Crabeater seals (*Lobodon carcinophagus*) grow to much more than 7 feet (2.1 m) long and live along the edge of the pack ice. They feed mainly on krill, shrimplike animals.

The Weddell seal (*Leptonychotes weddelli*) is one of the larger seals, about 9 feet (2.7 m) long, and feeds on fish. It can dive deeper than any other seal and stay submerged longer. Scientists know this because they can attach instruments and a radio to seals to track their movements. Individual Weddell seals have been known to dive to 2,000 feet (600 m) and remain under water for 73 minutes.

The only predators Antarctic seals must avoid are leopard seals, which sometimes attack other seals and killer whales.

A PAIR OF ADELIE PENGUINS *(Pygoscelis adeliae) (left)* **with their nest made from pebbles. The eggs rest on the pebbles, so they do not touch the ground, where they could be harmed by melting ice and snow.**

AN EMPEROR PENGUIN *(Aptenodytes forsteri) (right),* **the largest of the penguins, with its chick, which it rests on its feet.**

PENGUIN SPECIES *(below),* **drawn to show size variation. From left to right: emperor, chinstrap** *(Pygoscelis antarctica),* **Schlegel's** *(Eudyptes schlegeli),* **and the little blue penguin** *(Eudyptula minor).*

A PAIR OF ROCKHOPPER PENGUINS *(Eudyptes crestatus)* *(left)* with their chick. Rockhoppers feed on crustaceans. They are the most aggressive of all penguins.

A PAIR OF KING PENGUINS *(Aptenodytes patagonicus)* *(below left)*. One is arranging its egg on its feet, which is where it will remain while being incubated. The bird is able to shuffle around rather awkwardly.

A PAIR OF ADELIE PENGUINS *(below)* greeting each another. With so many birds in the rookery, such rituals help partners to recognize one another.

Survival of the Polar Regions

With their harsh climate, extensive ice, and barren ground the polar regions look as though they have always existed and will always remain just as we see them today. Yet they are fragile environments, where even minor disturbance can cause great change.

A MOBILE LABORATORY *(opposite)* in Antarctica from which scientists study emperor penguins without disturbing them. The scientists will return to one of the many permanent research stations. Care is now taken to make sure staff from the stations cause no pollution or damage to wildlife.

At 12:04 A.M. on March 24, 1989, the oil tanker *Exxon Valdez* ran aground in Prince William Sound on the south coast of Alaska, spilling nearly 11 million gallons (42 million liters) of oil. This formed a slick that contaminated about 1,000 miles (1,600 km) of coastline.

Oil is poisonous to birds and mammals that swallow it as they try to clean it from the feathers and fur. It also clogs the pores in the leaves through which plants absorb the carbon dioxide they need in photosynthesis (the process of producing sugars using the energy of sunlight) and through which they release oxygen, a waste product of photosynthesis.

In most parts of the world oil can be cleaned up fairly quickly, but the *Exxon Valdez* spilled its oil in a region where in winter the ground freezes hard, making it impossible to scrape up the oil. In the following spring the ice melts, and more oil is released.

In the clean-up operation booms were used to contain the oil at sea, detergents were used to break it down, and it was scraped from the beach. A new method, "bioremediation," was also used. Farm fertilizer was spread on the beach to nourish bacteria that can feed on oil. Their numbers increased and they "ate" both fertilizer and oil.

The White Sea and Barents Sea off the northwest coast of Russia have also been polluted by wastes dumped from naval installations and leaked from deteriorating ships.

The Impact of People

People have always lived inside the Arctic Circle, but until recently Antarctica has never been populated. Today there are many scientific research stations. The American McMurdo Station, the largest, is the size of a small town. In summer its population reaches about 1,200.

Like any settlement, these stations produce wastes of all kinds, and disposing of them is not easy. With the sea and ground frozen solid and temperatures rarely rising above freezing, anything that is thrown away simply remains where it falls, and soot and dust from burning fuel can contaminate surface snow. A few years ago scientists in the Antarctic agreed to implement controls. Wastes are now collected and shipped back to the home country, and containers have been designed for waste fuel oil, lubricants, and laboratory chemicals.

Controls have also been agreed by governments. Antarctica is believed to possess large reserves of coal and valuable minerals. Under the Antarctic Treaty, however, any mining activity in Antarctica is forbidden.

Tourists are more difficult to control, and Antarctica is becoming more popular as a tourist destination. Reaching Antarctica involves a long,

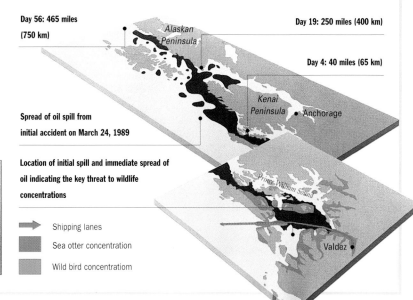

THE PATH OF THE *EXXON VALDEZ*. In 1989 the oil tanker *Exxon Valdez* ran aground in Prince William Sound off the south coast of Alaska spilling some of its cargo. The maps show the location of the accident and how the oil spread, carried northwest by tides, winds, and currents. The disaster killed thousands of marine mammals and a quarter of a million birds; the full extent of the damage is not yet known.

Day 56: 465 miles (750 km)

Day 19: 250 miles (400 km)

Day 4: 40 miles (65 km)

Alaskan Peninsula

Kenai Peninsula • Anchorage

Spread of oil spill from initial accident on March 24, 1989

Location of initial spill and immediate spread of oil indicating the key threat to wildlife concentrations

Prince William Sound

Valdez

0 ___ 300 km

0 ___ 300 miles

ALASKA

Alaskan Peninsula

Anchorage •

Valdez •

→ Shipping lanes

Sea otter concentration

Wild bird concentratiom

expensive journey and, not surprisingly, visitors want value for their money. They want to see the scenery, watch whales and seals, and, most of all, they want to see the penguins. Penguins are not used to humans and do not run away, so it is easy to move among them. There is a risk, however, that they may abandon eggs or that chicks will be separated from their parents. If this happens, the penguin populations may start to decrease. An additional problem is visitors leaving rubbish behind.

CLIMATE CHANGE

Many scientists fear that certain gases that are released into the air may cause the climates of the world to grow warmer during the next century. This is because "greenhouse gases" such as carbon dioxide, methane, nitrous oxide, ozone, and chlorofluorocarbons (CFCs) allow solar radiation to pass, but absorb some of the heat the Earth radiates when it is warmed. They then radiate the heat, warming the air. This is called the greenhouse effect because it is rather like the way that the glass of a greenhouse lets heat in but not out. The amount of these gases in the air has increased over the last century, primarily as a result of burning fossil fuels—coal, oil, and natural gas. Governments are now working on reducing these emissions.

If the amount of these gases were to double, average temperatures might increase by about 1.8°–6.3°F (1°–3.5°C), and sea levels by 6–37 inches (15–95 cm). This doubling might occur by the year 2100. The rise in sea level would be due mainly to the expansion of the oceans as

their water warms. To a lesser extent it would also be caused by the melting of glaciers.

A general warming would produce different effects in different places. No one can say what would happen. There are fears that in the Arctic it might lead to the widespread melting of the permafrost. This would alter the environment and threaten the tundra. Eventually, it would be replaced by coniferous forest.

Along the coast of Antarctica warmer conditions might cause the ice shelves to break up. This would not raise sea levels because shelf ice is already part of the sea. Were the ice sheets themselves to start melting, however, they would add meltwater to the oceans, and sea levels would rise; islands would disappear, and coastal areas would then be flooded. It is very unlikely that the Antarctic ice sheet would melt. It has existed for millions of years and survived periods in which the climate was warmer than is now being predicted. It is possible, though, that the Greenland ice sheet might become smaller.

One result of the warmer air would be that more water would evaporate. This would rise and condense to form clouds (which would cool the surface by shading it), so there would be more rain and snow. In the polar regions an increase in snowfall would make the ice sheets thicker. Far from causing a rise in sea level, this might make sea levels fall.

It may be that any climate change as a result of the greenhouse effect would be too small to have any effect. But the polar regions are still at risk from pollution and human disturbance to the wildlife that inhabits them. We need to take action to ensure that their remarkable scenery, plants, and animals will be preserved.

GREENLAND, where the inland ice sheet covers 708,000 square miles (1,833,700 sq. km) to an average depth of 5,000 feet (1,525 m). If all this ice melted as a result of global warming, sea levels would rise dramatically.

Glossary

ablation The removal of snow and ice by melting or sublimation.

alga A simple green plant that lacks true leaves, stem, and root. Many algae are single-celled; some are multicelled. Seaweeds are algae.

amphibian A vertebrate animal of the class Amphibia. The young develop in water, although the adults may live on land. Frogs, toads, newts, and salamanders are amphibians.

Antarctic Circle The line of latitude 66°30'S.

Arctic Circle The line of latitude 66°30'N.

bacteria Microscopic organisms, most of which are single-celled, that are found in air, water, and soil everywhere. Different types vary in shape and way of life.

biome A large region throughout which living conditions for plants and animals are broadly similar, so the region can be classified according to its vegetation type.

bioremediation The use of natural processes or organisms to improve the quality of an environment. For example, spilled oil might be cleared by applying fertilizer to stimulate the growth of bacteria that feed on oil.

carnivore An animal that feeds exclusively on other animals.

consumer An organism that is unable to manufacture its own food from simple ingredients but must obtain it by eating (consuming) other organisms.

convection Transfer of heat through a liquid or gas by the movement of the liquid or gas.

dew point temperature The temperature at which water vapor condenses and liquid water evaporates. Dew point temperature varies according to the amount of water vapor present in the air (the humidity).

ecology The study of the relationships among living organisms in a defined area and between the organisms and the nonliving features of their surroundings.

ecosystem A community of living organisms and their nonliving environment within a defined area. This may be of any size. A forest may be studied as an ecosystem and so may a drop of water.

equinox One of the two occasions each year when the Sun crosses the equator and day and night are of equal length.

eutrophic Highly enriched in nutrients.

frazil ice Ice that forms small plates rather than continuous sheets.

frost shattering The breaking of rock into fragments by the expansion of water as it freezes inside crevices or other spaces within the rock.

fungus A soft-bodied organism that obtains nutrients by absorbing them from its surroundings. Fungi are neither plants nor animals but constitute a kingdom of their own, the Fungi.

gill 1 The organ with which an aquatic animal obtains oxygen from water. It consists of thin membranes with a large surface area over which water flows. Oxygen passes from the water through the walls of blood vessels in the gill membrane and into the blood. Most aquatic animals have two gills. **2** A bladelike structure in the fruiting body of a fungus (such as a toadstool or mushroom) from which spores are released.

glacier A layer of ice made by the compression of snow due to the weight of overlying snow that accumulates year after year. Most glaciers spread by flowing. A glacier covering a wide area is called an ice sheet; one confined by the sides of a valley is called a valley glacier.

global warming A rise in the average atmospheric temperature, especially such a rise due to the absorption of heat by greenhouse gases emitted as a consequence of human activities.

greenhouse gases Gases present in the atmosphere that are transparent to short-wave solar radiation but partially opaque to long-wave radiation emitted from the surface of the Earth. The most important greenhouse gases are water vapor, carbon dioxide, methane, nitrous oxide, ozone, and chlorofluoro-carbons.

ground water Water below ground that fills all the spaces between soil particles, saturating the soil.

hanging valley A valley that joins a larger valley and has a floor higher than the floor of the valley it joins. If a river flows through a hanging valley, it will enter the larger valley as a waterfall. Hanging valleys are found where a glacier has widened and deepened the larger valley.

harem A group of two or more adult females that mate exclusively with a single male.

herbivore An animal that feeds exclusively on plants.

ice age A period during which ice sheets extended from polar regions much farther than they do at present. There have been many ice ages in the course of the Earth's history.

iceberg A large block of ice, floating freely at sea, that has broken away from the edge of a glacier or ice shelf.

ice sheet A layer of ice that covers a large area, usually about 20,000 square miles (52,000 sq. km), to a considerable depth.

ice shelf Part of an ice sheet that extends beyond the coast and over the sea, terminating in a cliff of ice. Near the coast the shelf is in contact with the sea bed, but in deeper water it floats. Vertical movements of the tides and waves cause sections to break away as icebergs.

insectivore An animal that feeds mainly or exclusively on insects.

invertebrate An animal that does not have a backbone.

irruption A sudden change in the density of the population of an organism, most commonly by migration, so that population density decreases in one area and increases in another.

lichen A plantlike organism consisting of a fungus and either an alga or a cyanobacterium (a bacterium that carries out photosynthesis) living in close association. The visible part of a lichen may be crustlike, scaly, leafy, or shrubby.

lung The organ of respiration in air-breathing vertebrates. In land-dwelling mollusks (snails and slugs), the part of the body involved in respiration.

melon A protuberance at the front of the head found in many species of toothed whales. It is filled with a waxy substance and is thought to perform some function connected with echolocation.

moraine A mass of rock debris that has been piled up by the movement of a glacier. Left as a surface deposit by a retreating glacier, it is called a "ground" moraine. Deposited at the leading edge of a glacier, it is called an "end" or "terminal" moraine. Deposited at the sides of a glacier, it is a "lateral" moraine. Deposited between two merging glaciers, it is a "medial" moraine.

muskeg An area of bog found in the taiga. It usually has bog moss (*Sphagnum* species) and cotton sedge (*Eriophorum* species) and sometimes a few stunted trees.

oasis An ice-free area in Antarctica. Oases are also called dry valleys.

omnivore An animal that eats food derived from both plants and animals.

pack ice A large area of sea ice that forms where ice floes are packed tightly together.

pancake ice Sea ice in the form of pieces that are rounded by constantly bumping and rubbing against each other.

parasite An organism that lives on the surface, or inside the body, of another organism that is known as the host. The parasite is usually smaller than its host and gets food, shelter, or some other necessity from it. The effects of the parasite on its host may range from none at all to severe illness or even death.

permafrost Ground where the temperature has remained below freezing for at least two consecutive winters and the intervening summer.

photosynthesis The series of chemical reactions by which green plants manufacture sugars, obtaining hydrogen from water and carbon from carbon dioxide, the energy driving the reactions being provided by light that is absorbed by chlorophyll.

phytoplankton *See* plankton.

pingo A dome-shaped hill the core of which is of ice.

plane of the ecliptic An imaginary disk the circumference of which is defined by the path traveled by the Earth in its orbit around the Sun.

plankton The small organisms that live near the surface of water and drift with movements of the water. They include single-celled plants (phytoplankton) and small animals (zooplankton), some of which are the larvae of fish and crustaceans.

precession of the equinoxes The westward movement of the Earth's rotational axis around a line at right-angles to the plane of the ecliptic. The Earth's axis wobbles like a spinning top that is not quite upright; this alters the days of the year on which the Sun is directly overhead at the equator (the equinoxes).

predator An organism that obtains food by consuming another organism. Most predators are animals that chase, overpower, and kill their prey, but insectivorous plants are also predators.

producer An organism, such as a green plant, that assembles large, complex substances from simple ingredients. These may then be eaten by consumers. On land the main producers are green plants; in water the main producers are phytoplankton (*see* plankton).

respiration 1 The oxidation of carbon to carbon dioxide in cells with the release of energy. **2** The action of breathing.

snout The lower end of a glacier, which is often turned up and pressed against moraine.

sublimation The process of changing directly from a solid to a gaseous state, without passing through a liquid phase.

taiga The Russian name for the belt of coniferous forest that stretches across northern Eurasia. The name is often applied also to the similar North American forest (otherwise called the "boreal" forest). Some ecologists restrict the term "taiga" to the belt of open, parklike forest along the northern edge of the boreal forest.

transpiration The loss of water vapor through pores, called stomata in the leaves and lenticels in the stems, of green plants.

tropics Those parts of the world that lie between latitudes 23°30'N and 23°30'S. These latitudes mark the boundaries of the region within which the Sun is directly overhead at noon on at least one day each year.

The Tropic of Cancer is to the north of the equator and the Tropic of Capricorn to the south.

tundra The vegetation of the extensive, low-lying plain of the Arctic and similar smaller area of the Antarctic. It consists mainly of sedges (*Carex* species) and rushes (*Juncus* species), with some grasses, herbs, and low-growing woody plants.

vertebrate An animal that has a backbone. Vertebrates also have a bony skull containing the brain and a skeleton made from bone or cartilage. Fish, amphibians, reptiles, birds, and mammals are vertebrates.

water table The uppermost margin of the ground water, below which the soil is saturated and above which it is not, although it is still wet.

weathering The physical and chemical processes by which rocks and minerals are broken down to particles of varying sizes, and soluble compounds are released into water.

zooplankton *See* plankton.

Further Reading

Basics of Environmental Science by Michael Allaby. Routledge.

Biology by Neil A. Campbell. The Benjamin/Cummings Publishing Co. Inc.

The Encyclopedia of Birds edited by Christopher M. Perrins and Alex L.A. Middleton. Facts on File.

The Encyclopedia of Insects edited by Christopher O'Toole. Facts on File.

The Encyclopedia of Mammals edited by David Macdonald. Facts on File.

The Encyclopedia of Reptiles and Amphibians edited by Tim Halliday and Kraig Adler. Facts on File.

Flowering Plants of the World edited by V.H. Heywood. Oxford University Press, New York.

Green Planet edited by David M. Moore. Cambridge University Press.

The Hunters by Philip Whitfield. Simon and Schuster.

Hutchinson Encyclopedia of the Earth edited by Peter J. Smith. Hutchinson.

The Lie of the Land edited by K.J. Gregory. Oxford University Press, New York.

Longman Illustrated Animal Encyclopedia edited by Philip Whitfield. Guild Publishing.

The Oxford Encyclopedia of Trees of the World edited by Bayard Hora. Oxford University Press, New York.

Planet Earth: Cosmology, Geology, and the Evolution of Life and Environment by Cesare Emiliani. Cambridge University Press.

Snakes of the World by Chris Mattison. Blandford Press Ltd.

The Science of Ecology by Richard Brewer. Saunders College Publishing, Harcourt Brace College Publishers.

Dangerous Weather: Blizzards by Michael Allaby. Facts on File.

The Natural History of the USSR by Algirdas Knystautas. Century Hutchinson.

Web sites:

Polar Regions home page, with links to many countries bordering the Arctic Circle and to Antarctic research organizations, is at: http://www.stud.unit.no/~sveinw/arctic/

Arctic Circle, a University of Connecticut site with many links, is at: http://www.arcticcircle.uconn.edu/

Photographic Acknowledgments

10–11 A.G.E. Fotostock/Images Colour Library; **17** Norbert Schwirtz/Bruce Coleman Limited; **20** Mike Read/Swift Picture Library; **22–23** Fred Bruemmer; **24** B. Klingwall; **27** Vadim Gippenreiter; **29** Bob & Clara Calhoun/Bruce Coleman Limited; **31** Fred Bruemmer; **35** S. Carlsson; **36** Fred Bruemmer; **38–39** Joel Bennett/Survival Anglia/Oxford Scientific Films; **43** Fred Bruemmer; **53** Whittle/Ecoscene; **55** J. Mackinnon/Planet Earth Pictures; **Cover pictures:** *top:* Fritz Prenzel/Bruce Coleman Limited; *bottom:* David Hughes/Bruce Coleman Limited; *globe motif:* Terra Forma™ Copyright© 1995–1997 Andromeda Interactive Ltd.

While every effort has been made to trace the copyright holders of illustrations reproduced in this book, the publishers will be pleased to rectify any omissions or inaccuracies.

Set Index

Page numbers in *italics* refer to illustrations; volume numbers are in **bold**.